Managing Reality
Book Three
Managing the Contract

Third edition

Other titles in the Managing Reality series:

Managing Reality. Book One: Introduction to the Engineering and Construction Contract. Third edition (2017)
Bronwyn Mitchell and Barry Trebes. ISBN 978-0-7277-6182-8

Managing Reality. Book Two: Procuring an Engineering and Construction Contract. Third edition (2017)
B. Mitchell and B. Trebes. ISBN 978-0-7277-6184-2

Managing Reality. Book Four: Managing Change. Third edition (2017)
B. Mitchell and B. Trebes. ISBN 978-0-7277-6188-0

Managing Reality. Book Five: Managing Procedures. Third edition (2017)
B. Mitchell and B. Trebes. ISBN 978-0-7277-6190-3

Managing Reality

Book Three

Managing the Contract

Third edition

Bronwyn Mitchell and Barry Trebes

Published by ICE Publishing, One Great George Street, Westminster, London SW1P 3AA.

Full detail of ICE Publishing representatives and distributors can be found at:
www.icebookshop.com/bookshop_contact.asp

Other titles by ICE Publishing:
NEC4: The Role of the Project Manager
B. Mitchell and B. Trebes. ISBN 978-0-7277-6353-2
NEC4: The Role of the Supervisor
B. Mitchell and B. Trebes. ISBN 978-0-7277-6355-6
NEC3 and NEC4 Compared
R. Gerrard. ISBN 978-0-7277-6201-6

www.icebookshop.com

A catalogue record for this book is available from the British Library

ISBN 978-0-7277-6186-6

Commissioning Editor: Michael Fenton
Production Editor: Madhubanti Bhattacharyya
Market Development Executive: Elizabeth Hobson

FSC
www.fsc.org
MIX
Paper from
responsible sources
FSC® C019520

Typeset by Academic + Technical, Bristol
Index created by Laurence Errington
Printed and bound by NOVOPRINT S.A., Spain

Contents

Preface

In the preface to the first edition of *Managing Reality*, in 2005, we set out our aims and aspirations for 'managing reality'. These were as follows:

- to add and contribute to the body of knowledge on the use of the NEC Engineering and Construction Contract (ECC)
- to provide a set of books that focuses on the 'how to' – how to manage and administer the ECC contract
- to present as a five-part book series that covers both the needs of the student professional or prospective client, through to the novice practitioner and experienced user
- to provide a rounded view of the ECC, whatever your discipline, on both sides of the contractual relationship
- to enable everyone to realise the business benefits from using the NEC suite of contracts generally and the ECC in particular.

Managing Reality does not attempt to give a legal treatise or a blow-by-blow review of each and every clause. It is intended to be complementary to other publications, which give excellent theoretical and legal perspectives.

This book is about dealing with the reality of real life projects: managing reality.

The feedback and support we have received since the first publication of *Managing Reality* in 2005 has been universally positive, and we would like to thank all of you who have bought and used it since its first publication.

We have greatly enjoyed updating and working on this third edition, and we hope that these books continue to provide a useful body of knowledge on the use of the NEC4 ECC.

Bronwyn Mitchell and Barry Trebes
2017

Foreword

A key objective of the first edition of *Managing Reality* was to provide a five-part book series to meet the needs of students, prospective clients, novice practitioners and experienced users. Satisfying such diverse needs is an ambitious objective for any text.

Does *Managing Reality* achieve its stated aim? I believe that the answer to this is a resounding 'yes'. In my view, the calibre of authorship is exceptional. All levels of and types of readership from the uninitiated to the experienced professional will derive considerable benefit from this text. Although written in a very accessible style, there is no skimping on detail or on addressing difficult issues. The worked examples are particularly helpful. *Managing Reality* should be your prime aid from the moment you are considering whether or not to use an NEC contract right through to using and operating the contract.

But *Managing Reality* is much more than simply a 'how to' guide. It seeks to deliver a clear message that NEC contracts cannot be used to their full potential unless one is prepared to ditch one's knowledge and experience of traditional contracting. For example, emphasis is placed on the fact that certainty and predictability are the hallmarks of NEC contracts. Open-ended and subjective phrases and concepts have no place in NEC contracting.

I am privileged to be associated with this third edition of *Managing Reality*. Its publication is very timely since it coincides with the publication of the NEC4 suite of contracts. This new edition of the NEC suite is a reflection of the dominant position that NEC contracts now have both in the UK and in many other countries. It will continue to support those who need help overcoming any reservations about using NEC contracts, and reinforce existing users in their continued use of these ground-breaking contracts.

Professor Rudi Klein
President, NEC Users' Group

Acknowledgements

We would like to thank the following individuals and companies who have supported this book.

For their active participation in this book we would like to thank

- Professor Rudi Klein (SEC Group Chief Executive) for writing the Foreword
- Dr Robert N. Hunter of Hunter and Edgar Edinburgh for his thoughts and suggested revisions for this third edition
- Michael Fenton, the ICE commissioning editor, for his enthusiasm and patience
- Richard Patterson of Mott MacDonald
- everyone who has given feedback on this book since 2005.

And our continued gratitude to those who provided support and input into the first edition of *Managing Reality*:

- Mike Attridge, of Ellenbrook Consulting, who reviewed this book on behalf of the authors
- David H. Williams, who provided guidance and support in the development of the first edition of this book
- everyone at Needlemans Limited Construction Consultants (now part of the Mott MacDonald Group)
- everyone at MPS Limited with whom Needlemans Limited worked to develop the first web-based management system for the NEC in 2000.

Finally, we would like to thank our family and friends for their ongoing support, understanding and patience.

Series contents

The following outlines the content of the five books in the series.

- emphasises the importance of early dispute resolution to the successful outcome of a contract
- considers the common sources of dispute
- considers how the ECC has been designed to reduce the incidence of disputes
- examines how the ECC provides for the resolution of disputes
- looks at the implications for the dispute resolution process as a result of the HGCR Act as amended
- looks at ECC changes in relation to adjudication.

Book 4 Managing Reality: Managing Change

Chapter 1   Compensation events
This chapter describes

- the compensation events contained within the ECC
- procedure for administering compensation events
- roles played by the two main parties to the contract in relation to compensation events.

Appendix 1   Compensation event procedure

Chapter 2   Schedule of Cost Components and Short Schedule of Cost Components
This chapter discusses aspects relating to the full SCC and its short version, the SSCC, including

- when the SCC and SSCC are used
- how the SCC and SSCC interact with the payment clauses
- Defined Cost
- the Fee
- the components of cost included under the SCC and SSCC
- Contract Data part two.

Appendix 2   Example quotations for compensation events

Appendix 3   Example people cost calculations

Appendix 4   Comparison between traditional preliminaries build-up and how they relate to the Schedule of Cost Components and the Short Schedule of Cost Components

Appendix 5   Interrelationship between the *Contractor's* and the Subcontractor's *share* on target cost contracts

Book 5 Managing Reality: Managing Procedures

Chapter 1   ECC Management: Procedures
This chapter brings together all the aspects discussed in previous chapters in Books One to Four of the *Managing Reality* series. This chapter provides the 'how to' part of the series. It introduces some example pro formas for use with the ECC. Unless detailed separately due to a complex procedure, replies are described under the relevant action.

For quick reference, this chapter may be read on its own. It does not, however, detail the reasons for carrying out the actions, or the clause numbers that should be referred to in order to verify the actions in accordance with the contract. These are described in detail in the other books that form part of this series.

Managing the Contract
ISBN 978-0-7277-6186-6

Introduction

General

This series of books will provide the people who are actually using the Engineering and Construction Contract (ECC) in particular, and the New Engineering Contract (NEC) suite in general, practical guidance as to how to prepare and manage an ECC contract with confidence and knowledge of the effects of their actions on the contract and the Parties.

Each book in the series addresses a different area of the management of an ECC contract:

- Book One – *Managing Reality: Introduction to the Engineering and Construction Contract*
- Book Two – *Managing Reality: Procuring an Engineering and Construction Contract*
- Book Three – *Managing Reality: Managing the Contract*
- Book Four – *Managing Reality: Managing Change*
- Book Five – *Managing Reality: Managing Procedures.*

Book One (*Managing Reality: Introduction to the Engineering and Construction Contract*) is for those who are considering using the ECC but need further information, or those who are already using the ECC but need further insight into its rationale. It therefore focuses on the fundamental cultural changes and mind-shift that are required to successfully manage the practicalities of the ECC in use.

Book Two (*Managing Reality: Procuring an Engineering and Construction Contract*) is for those who need to know how to procure an ECC contract. It covers in practical detail the invitations to tender, evaluation of submissions, which option to select, how to complete the Contract Data and how to prepare the Scope. The use of this guidance is appropriate for clients, contractors (including subcontractors) and construction professionals generally.

Book Three (*Managing Reality: Managing the Contract*) is essentially for those who use the contract on a daily basis, covering the detail of practical management such as paying the contractor, reviewing the programme, ensuring the quality of the *works*, and dispute resolution. Both first-time and experienced practitioners will benefit from this book.

Book Four (*Managing Reality: Managing Change*) is for those who are managing change under the contract; whether for the client or the contractor (or subcontractor), the management of change is often a major challenge whatever the form of contract. The ECC deals with change in a different way to other, more traditional forms. This book sets out the steps to efficiently and effectively manage change, bridging the gap between theory and practice.

Book Five (*Managing Reality: Managing Procedures*) gives step-by-step guidance on how to apply the most commonly used procedures, detailing the actions needed by all Parties to comply with the contract. Anyone administering the contract will benefit from this book.

Background

The ECC could be termed a 'modern contract' in that it seeks to holistically align the setting up of a contract to match business needs as opposed to writing a contract that merely administers construction events.

The whole ethos of the ECC, and the NEC suite generally, is one of simplicity of language and clarity of requirement. It is important that the roles and responsibilities of all of those involved in the contract are equally clear in definition and ownership.

When looking at the ECC for the first time it is easy to believe that it is relatively straightforward and simple. However, this apparent simplicity belies the need for the people involved to think about their project and their role, and how the ECC can deliver their particular contract strategy.

The ECC provides a structured flexible framework for setting up an appropriate form of contract whatever the selected procurement route. The fundamental requirements are as follows:

- The Scope – quality and completeness: what are you asking the *Contractor* to do?
- The Site Information: what are the site conditions that the *Contractor* will find?
- The Contract Data – key objectives for completion (e.g. start date, completion date and programme): when do you want it completed?

The details contained in this series of books will underline the relevance and importance of the above three fundamental requirements.

The structure of the books

Each chapter starts with a synopsis of what is included in that chapter. Throughout the book there are shaded 'practical tip' boxes that immediately point the user towards important reminders for using the ECC (see example below).

> Clarity and completeness of the Scope is fundamental.

There are also unshaded boxes that contain examples to illustrate the text (see example below).

> Imagine a situation in which the *Supervisor* notifies the *Contractor* that the reinstatement of carriageways on a utility diversion project is not to the highway authority's usual standards. However, the Scope is silent about the reinstatement.
>
> The test of a Defect is also whether the work is in accordance with the applicable law. In this instance, the reinstatement is not in accordance with the Road and Street Works Act 1991.

Other diagrams and tables are designed to maintain interest and provide another medium of explanation. There are also standard forms for use in the administration and management of the contract, together with examples.

Throughout the books, the following terms have been used in a specific way:

- NEC is the abbreviation for the suite of New Engineering Contracts and it is not the name of any single contract
- ECC is the abbreviation for the contract in the NEC suite called the Engineering and Construction Contract.

The NEC4 suite comprises the

- Engineering and Construction Contract
- Engineering and Construction Subcontract
- Engineering and Construction Short Contract
- Engineering and Construction Short Subcontract
- Professional Service Contract
- Professional Service Short Contract
- Term Service Contract
- Term Service Short Contract
- Supply Contract
- Supply Short Contract
- Framework Contract
- Dispute Resolution Service Contract
- Design Build and Operate Contract
- Alliance Contract – consultative version.

Managing the Contract
ISBN 978-0-7277-6186-6

Chapter 1
Payment procedures in the Engineering and Construction Contract

Synopsis

This chapter discusses the following:

- the payment procedure, including
  - when the *Contractor's* application for payment is submitted
  - when assessments take place
  - when the payment certificate is issued
  - how invoicing is carried out
  - when payment takes place

- the effects of option Y(UK)2, taking into account the Housing Grants, Construction and Regeneration Act 1996 as amended.

1.1. Introduction

One of the biggest changes made by the ECC in terms of payment is that it is the *Project Manager's* job to assess the amount due to the *Contractor*. The *Contractor* is required to submit an application for payment, and the *Project Manager* is required to consider it in assessing the amount due, but it is still the *Project Manager's* duty to assess the amount due and to certify payment. The lack of detailed application for payment from a *Contractor*, which includes the Price for the Work Done to Date, could hinder the *Project Manager* in their assessment of the amount due, particularly for contract Options C, D and E.

Another point to note is that there are no contractual invoicing procedures.

Lastly, the deductions made from the amount due are made by the *Project Manager* and are obliged to be made by them. There is no discretion on their part not to retain one-quarter of the Price for Work Done to Date in assessments of the amount due if a first programme has not been received, and there is no discretion not to deduct delay damages if Completion is late and Option X7 applies to the contract. It is not the *Client* who makes these deductions but the *Project Manager*.

It is worth noting here that the power for the *Project Manager* to act in this way may not align with the internal procedures of the *Client*. Sometimes the client or finance officer of a business will wish to retain these powers for themselves. This needs to be addressed for the ECC to work effectively.

The allocation of these powers in the ECC is a reflection of the importance that the contract places on the *Project Manager*, and it emphasises the significance of the selection procedures for a *Project Manager* and that they should have the power and authority to act as described in the contract.

1.2. The payment procedure

The following is a breakdown of the payment procedure as outlined in the *conditions of contract*. The choice of main Option will affect what appears in the application for payment and the assessment of the amount due, but will not necessarily affect the procedure.

1.2.1 The *Contractor's* application for payment

The *Contractor* submits an application for payment to the *Project Manager* before the assessment date, setting out the amount that the *Contractor* considers is due at the assessment date (clause 50.2). The *Contractor's* application for payment includes details of how the amount has been assessed, and is in the form stated in the Scope.

It is to the *Project Manager's* advantage if the Scope provides that the *Contractor's* application for payment follows a certain format that mirrors the way the *Project Manager* will set out its assessment of the amount due. For example, in Options C, D and E, the *Contractor* is paid their Defined Cost plus its Fee; that is, its interim payments are based on the Schedule of Cost Components and not on some immediately determinable pricing tool such as an *activity schedule* or *bill of quantities*. Therefore, for these Options, the Scope may require the *Contractor* to provide its application using the headings and information required by the Schedule of Cost Components.

> The *Contractor* is required to submit an application for payment.

The *Contractor's* assessment comprises (clause 50.3)

> - The Price for Work Done to Date
> - plus other amounts to be paid to the *Contractor*
> - less amounts to be paid by or retained from the *Contractor*.

The Scope may require the *Contractor* to show the Price for Work Done to Date as a cumulative amount, less previous payments, leaving a payment for the assessment date in question.

1.2.2 The assessment date

Assessments of the amount due by the *Project Manager* take place at each assessment date (clause 50.1).

1.2.2.1 The first assessment date

The first assessment date is decided by the *Project Manager* to suit the procedures of the Parties, and is not later than the *assessment interval* after the *starting date* (clause 50.1). There are three aspects to note about this clause:

- It is the *Project Manager* who decides the date of the first assessment, rather than the *conditions of contract* or the Parties.
- Although the *Project Manager* decides the date of the first assessment, it must suit the procedures of both the *Client* and the *Contractor*. In order to do this, input is required from the *Contractor* regarding what date would suit their procedures. This could take place at the start-up meeting, or by other communication prior to the *starting date*. The other assessment dates could be independent of this first date (they occur at the end of each *assessment interval*, and the *assessment interval* need not be related to the first assessment date). The occurrence of this first date need not affect later assessments.
- The first assessment date cannot be later than the *assessment interval* after the *starting date*. It is the *starting date* that is the important date here, not the start date on Site or *access dates*, as the *starting date* indicates the start of the contract and therefore facilitates payment for work done off Site prior to work starting on Site, such as manufacture or design.

1.2.2.2 Other assessment dates

- In the ECC, assessment dates other than the first assessment date occur at the end of each *assessment interval* until the *Supervisor* issues the Defects Certificate or the *Project Manager* issues a termination certificate (these two scenarios are in the alternative). The Defects Certificate is issued at the *defects date* if there are no notified Defects, or otherwise at the earlier of the end of the last *defect correction period* and the date when all notified Defects have been corrected (clause 44.3). This means that assessment dates in the ECC take place regularly, from Completion until the *defects date* or the end of the last *defect correction period* or the date when all notified Defects have been corrected; that is, assessments should take place regularly during a period of approximately 1 year, even though there may have been no activity on the contract and an assessment is therefore not necessary. The *assessment interval* is identified in Contract Data part one, and is the key to the length of time between interim valuations of the project. Note that the trigger is the **end** of the *assessment interval*. Examples of *assessment interval*s are as follows:

  (*a*) **The *assessment interval* is 4 weeks**. Because not all months are 4 weeks long, the end of a 4-week period will creep earlier and earlier in the month, and it will not be long before the end of the 4-week period is somewhere in the middle of a month. This is unlikely to be convenient for either Party; however, some organisations operate 13 periods of 4 weeks.

  (*b*) **The *assessment interval* is one calendar month**. The end of a calendar month is more convenient and is also more definable without resorting to calendars to determine when the date will fall. If, for example, the *assessment interval* is 'one calendar month' (as stated in Contract Data part one), then the assessment dates will be at the end of each calendar month, irrespective of the day of the week on which the end of the calendar month falls. If even more preciseness is required, the Parties could agree to the last Friday of each month, or whatever is suitable to their procedures, in which case the *assessment interval* is the period between the last Friday in the previous calendar month to the last Friday in the next calendar month.

  (*c*) **The *assessment interval* is the period between relevant dates in the schedule of project dates included in the Scope**. Some employers, recognising that the project procedures could correlate with the accounting department's requirements, compile a schedule of project dates showing
    – when the *Contractor* submits their application for payment
    – the assessment date
    – the date of the payment certificate
    – the date of invoice (see below)
    – the date for payment.

This matrix of project dates makes it quite clear to all parties concerned when documents are required to be submitted.

■ A final assessment takes place no later than 4 weeks after the *Supervisor* issues the Defects Certificate or 13 weeks after the *Project Manager* issues a termination certificate.

1.2.3 Assessing the amount due

At each assessment date as identified above, the *Project Manager* assesses the amount due (clauses 50.1 and 50.2). The *Project Manager* assesses the amount due in the same way that the *Contractor* would; that is, by assessing the cumulative Price for Work Done to Date and then the amount now due.

The *Project Manager* assesses the amount due.

1.2.3.1 What is included in the assessment

The amount due assessed by the *Project Manager* is the Price for Work Done to Date, plus other amounts to be paid by the *Contractor* less amounts to be paid by or retained from the *Contractor* (clause 50.5). Any value added tax (VAT) or sales tax that the law requires the *Client* to pay to the *Contractor* is added to any payment made under the contract. This is similar to the way in which a *Contractor* would be expected to submit an application for payment.

'If the *Contractor* submits an application for payment before the assessment date, the amount due at the assessment date is

■ the Price for Work Done to Date,
■ plus other amounts to be paid to the *Contractor*
■ less amounts to be paid by or retained from the *Contractor*.' (clause 50.3)

'In assessing the amount due, the *Project Manager* considers an application for payment submitted by the *Contractor* before the assessment date.' (clause 50.2)

'If the *Contractor* does not submit an application for payment before the assessment date, the amount due at the assessment date is the lesser of

■ the amount the *Project Manager* assesses as due at the assessment date, assessed as though the *Contractor* had submitted an application before the assessment date* and
■ the amount due at the previous assessment date.' (clause 50.4)

*That is, the Price for Work Done to Date plus other amounts to be paid to the *Contractor* minus amounts to be paid by or retained from the *Contractor*.

So, if the *Contractor* has not submitted an application for payment before the assessment date, and the *Project Manager* assesses the amount due as £100 000 and the last amount due at the previous assessment date is £80 000, then the £80 000 is taken as the amount due. This provides a significant incentive for the *Contractor* to submit an application for payment.

Alternatively, if the *Project Manager* assesses the amount due as £100 000, and the last amount due at the previous assessment date is £120 000, then the £100 000 is taken as the amount due.

The amount due can be summarised as follows:

■ The Price for Work Done to Date
■ plus other amounts to be paid to the *Contractor*
■ less amounts to be paid by or retained from the *Contractor* subtotal
■ less previous payments

Payment due for this application

■ plus VAT (to be added to payment)

Total to pay

- The Price for Work Done to Date is a defined term that depends on the main Option chosen as part of the *Client's* contract strategy. For example, in Option A, the Price for Work Done to Date is the total of the Prices for completed activities that are without Defects (clause 11.2(29)). The *Project Manager* should therefore take the main Option into account when assessing the amount due (more about this in Chapter 2 of Book Two).
- Other amounts to be paid to the *Contractor* could relate to an advanced payment (Option X14), a bonus for early Completion (Option X6), a correction of previous certificates, and interest due.
- Amounts to be paid by or retained from the *Contractor* could include retention (Option X16), the repayment of an advancement (Option X14), delay damages (Option X7) or the retention of 25% of the Price for Work Done to Date for a first programme showing the information that the contract requires was not submitted for acceptance by the *Contractor* (clause 50.5)
- Since the Price for Work Done to Date is the total to date, in order to calculate the amount due in the current assessment, previous payments should be deducted.
- VAT is to be shown separately, and is added to any payment (clause 51.5).

1.2.3.2 The programme

This section refers only to contracts where the *Client* has included the statement about a first programme in Contract Data *Part One*, and where the *Project Manager* can therefore expect to see a first programme submitted for acceptance after the Contract Date by the *Contractor* showing the information that the contract requires, including any additional information included in the Scope.

Contract Data part one, section 3, 'Time'

If no programme is identified in part two of the Contract Data

The period after the Contract Date within which the *Contractor* is to submit a first programme for acceptance is ....

This section does *not* apply where the *Client* has requested a programme to be submitted with the tender, and so has included the relevant statement about the programme in Contract Data part two and not Contract Data part one.

Contract Data part two, section 3, 'Time'

If a programme is to be identified in the Contract Data

The programme identified in the Contract Data is ....

If the *Client* has asked for an outline programme at tender stage, or a programme focusing on certain elements of the overall programme, the contract will need to make clear which programme the *Client* considers to be a first programme for the purposes of clause 50.5.

The *Project Manager* determines whether the *Contractor* has submitted a first programme for acceptance that shows the information required by the contract (clause 50.5). This would generally apply when the *Client* has asked for a first programme to be submitted after the Contract Date and the relevant statement has been included in Contract Data part one.

If the *Project Manager* has not received a first programme for acceptance showing the information that the contract requires, then a quarter (25%) – this is an obligation, not an option – of the Price for Work Done to Date (not 25% of the amount due) is retained in assessments of the amount due. Note that the criterion is not that the *Project Manager* has accepted the programme but that one has been submitted, showing all the information required by the contract, including the Scope.

> The *Contractor's* cash flow could suffer if they do not submit a first programme for acceptance when they are required to do so.

Where a programme was requested and submitted with the tender, this programme may not show all the information required by the contract, especially if that information was not available at the time of tender. It is unlikely, however, that the *Project Manager* would be able to use this lack of information as the reason for retaining one-quarter of the Price for Work Done to Date in assessments of the amount due, since clause 50.5 refers to situations where no programme was identified in the Contract Data; that is, the statements relating to the programme do not appear in Contract Data part two, but do appear in Contract Data part one. If, on the other hand, the *Contractor* was required to submit a first programme within a certain time period after the Contract Date, then the *Contractor* should ensure it is submitted at the latest by the first assessment date.

1.2.3.3 Interest

Note that it is the *Project Manager* who assesses the interest and includes it in the certificate for payment. The *Project Manager* should not wait for the *Contractor* to claim the interest. Interest is paid for five reasons:

1 If a certified payment is late, interest is assessed on the late payment and paid in the very next assessment (clause 51.2). The interest is assessed from the date when the payment should have been made to the date when it was made. This clause refers to a payment that was certified by the *Project Manager*; if the payment is made late, then interest is paid, but the clause does not differentiate the reason for the payment being late.

2 The same clause provides for a late payment that is late because the *Project Manager* has not issued a certificate that should be issued. Interest is assessed on the late payment and paid in the very next assessment (clause 51.2). The interest is assessed from the date when the payment should have been made to the date when it was made. The clause does not specifically pertain to the *Project Manager's* payment certificate, although it is implied. This part of clause 51.2 is in the alternative to the first part of the clause discussed in reason 1 above; that is, the assessment of interest only takes place once for a payment that is late, even if the reason is that the *Project Manager* did not issue a certificate that should have been issued.

3 If an amount due is corrected in a later certificate in relation to a mistake or a compensation event, interest is assessed on the correcting amount (clause 51.3) and paid in the assessment that includes the correcting amount. The interest is assessed from the date when the incorrect amount was certified to the date when the correcting amount is certified.

4 If an amount due is corrected in a later certificate because a payment was delayed by an unnecessary delay to a test or inspection done by the *Supervisor*, interest is assessed on the correcting amount (clause 51.3) and paid in the assessment that includes the correcting amount. The interest is assessed from the date when the incorrect amount was certified to the date when the correcting amount is certified.

5 If an amount due is corrected in a later certificate following a decision of the *Adjudicator* or *tribunal* or a recommendation of the Dispute Avoidance Board, interest is assessed on the correcting amount (clause 51.3) and paid in the assessment that includes the correcting amount. The interest is assessed from the date when the incorrect amount was certified to the date when the correcting amount is certified.

Interest is calculated on a daily basis at the *interest rate*, and is compounded annually (clause 51.4).

1.2.3.4 The time period for assessment

The *Project Manager* has less than a week in which to complete their assessment (since they have to issue a payment certificate within 1 week of each assessment date (clause 51.1)). This short time period may become too onerous for the *Project Manager*, particularly for contracts under Options C, D and E, where there would be insufficient time to examine fully the *Contractor's* application and all the supporting documentation.

A suggested course of action is that the *Project Manager* conducts a spot check of the application for payment that the *Contractor* is required to submit, and conducts later inspections of the *Contractor's* records that they are required to keep according to the Scope. This inspection process should be detailed in the Scope and adhered to by the *Project Manager* and their assistants. The *Project Manager* has the ability to correct any wrongly assessed amount due in a later payment certificate (clause 50.6), which gives the *Project Manager* the opportunity to make any changes post audit.

1.2.3.5 The details of assessment

In assessing the amount due, the *Project Manager* is required to consider an application for payment submitted by the *Contractor* before the assessment date.

If the *Contractor* has submitted an application for payment (clause 50.2), the amount due is the Price for Work Done to Date plus other amounts to be paid to the *Contractor*, less amounts to be paid or retained from the *Contractor*.

If the *Contractor* does not submit an application for payment before the assessment date, the amount due at the assessment date is the lesser of

- the amount that the *Project Manager* assesses as due at the assessment date, assessed as the *Contractor* had submitted the application before the assessment date
- the amount due at the previous assessment date.

So, if the *Project Manager* assesses that the amount due is £100 000 and the last amount due at the previous assessment date is £80 000, then the £80 000 is taken as the amount due. This provides a significant incentive for the *Contractor* to submit an application for payment.

Alternatively, if the *Project Manager* assesses the amount due as £100 000 and the last amount due at the previous assessment date is £102 000, then the £100 000 is taken as the amount due.

1.2.4 Certification

The *Project Manager* certifies a payment within 1 week of each assessment date (clause 51.1). The *Project Manager* includes with the payment certificate the details of how the amount due has been assessed by them. If any previous amount due was incorrect, it is corrected in a later payment certificate. Interest (on previous late payments or on correcting amounts) is included in later payment certificates (clauses 51.2 and 51.3). The *Project Manager* should voluntarily include interest in a payment certificate if previous payments were made late to the *Contractor*; the *Project Manager* should not wait for the *Contractor* to claim interest (an example of a payment certificate is included in Chapter 1 of Book Five). Any tax that the *Client* is legally obliged to pay is added to payments made under the contract (clause 51.5).

1.2.5 Invoices

Any invoice procedure dictated by the *Client* takes place at this stage.

None of the NEC contracts cater for invoicing as part of the payment procedure.

If the *Client* wishes to receive an invoice from the *Contractor* for the purposes of payment, then an invoice process will have to be introduced into the contract through either secondary Option Z or the Scope.

Many employers augment the payment procedure in the *conditions of contract* with other information that they prefer to receive and as described in the Scope. For example, some *Clients* may dictate how the *Contractor* should format their application for payment and what documents should accompany the application, such as, in the case of Options C, D or E, labour records, timesheets, plant records and the payroll. As part of the payment administration procedures, *Clients* could also include a section on invoicing, instructing the *Contractor* when to submit an invoice and what the invoice should contain. Some examples of what a *Client* may include in the Scope regarding invoicing procedures are listed below:

- To whom the invoice is to be addressed – possibly the *Client's* finance department within the *Client's* organisation.

- When the invoice should be submitted; for example, 'Invoices shall be submitted within 7 days of the date of the *Project Manager's* payment certificate or on the date stated on the attached schedule of project dates.'
- The sanction on a late invoice; for example, 'Payment shall be delayed by the number of days that the invoice is late.'
- What the invoice should show; for example, 'Invoices shall show the full amount claimed to date, deducting separately previous payments. The latest statement of account should accompany the invoice. Accounts shall be shown net of VAT, with the amount of VAT shown separately.'

Invoicing is usually an internal procedure that facilitates payment, and is not therefore, strictly speaking, a condition of contract. A *Client's* invoicing procedure normally coincides with the procedures required by their accounts department, and may therefore vary from client to client. Whatever the invoicing procedure, it takes place within the parameters of the interval between the assessment date and the payment date (or, in the case of Option Y(UK)2, the certificate date and the final date for payment), and care should be taken to ensure that a late invoice resulting in a late payment is not construed as a *Client's* default.

The ECC does not include an invoicing procedure.

Figure 1.1 Default time period in the contract

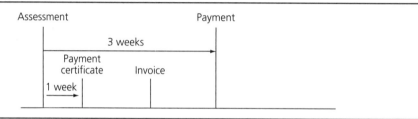

1.2.6 Payment

The *Client* makes payment a specified time after the assessment date. This may be 3 weeks (clause 51.2), which is the default in the *conditions of contract*, or the *Client* could use the CD1 entry to change the 3 week payment period to 4 or 5 weeks.

Note that the payment date is dependent on the assessment date and not the date of the payment certificate or the date of the invoice. None of the activities that takes place between

Figure 1.2 Payment procedures in the ECC

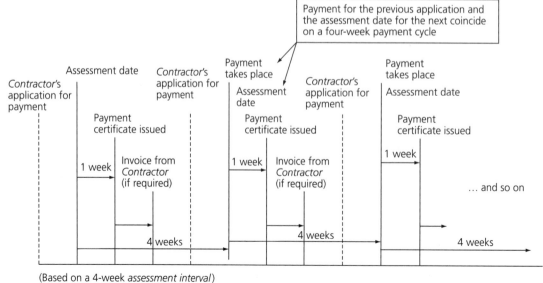

(Based on a 4-week *assessment interval*)

the assessment date and the payment date should delay payment. Additional clauses using Option Z or additional requirements in the Scope can be used to ensure that the *Client* is not in default when a payment is late as a result of a late invoice.

1.2.7 Representation of the payment procedure in the ECC

Figure 1.2 assumes that certified payment is made within 4 weeks of the assessment date, rather than the default 3 weeks in clause 51.2. A *Client* would need to include the time period (4 weeks) in Contract Data part one to effect this change.

Contract Data part one

If the period in which payments are made is not 3 weeks and Y(UK)2 is not used

The period within which payments are made is ....

1.3. How the ECC includes the HGCR Act

The ECC incorporates the Housing Grants, Construction and Regeneration Act 1996 (HGCR Act) as amended in two different places: payment changes in Option Y(UK)2 and adjudication changes in Option W2.

Adjudication is discussed in Chapter 4 of this book.

1.4. The effects of Y(UK)2
1.4.1 Periods for payment

Where the *Client* has determined that the HGCR Act as amended applies to the contract, and thus has chosen Option Y(UK)2 to apply to the contract, the payment procedure is affected.

Four concepts are introduced in Option Y(UK)2 and through the HGCR Act:

■ **The date on which the payment becomes due (the payment due date).** This is not the date on which payment has to be made but rather the date that marks that the payment is due to be paid some time in the future. The date on which a payment becomes due is 7 days after the assessment date (clause Y2.2 of Option Y(UK)2), and is the latest day by which the *Project Manager* must certify a payment (clause Y2.2 of Option Y(UK)2).

The due date is different from the final date for payment.

■ **The final date for payment.** This is the latest date by which each certified payment must be made. The final date for payment is a certain time period after the date on which the payment becomes due (rather than a certain period after the assessment date, as with the default *conditions of contract*). In the ECC, the final date for payment is 14 days after the date on which payment becomes due, or a different period if stated in the Contract Data (clause Y2.2 of Option Y(UK)2).
■ **The notified sum.** This is the sum included in the payment certificate as the sum that is due to be paid on the final date for payment. The Local Democracy, Economic Development and Construction Act 2009 which amended the 1996 Act provides further information about the notified sum.
■ **The prescribed period.** This is the number of days agreed between the Parties to be the period before the final date for payment. Clause Y2.3 of Option Y(UK)2 states that the prescribed period is 7 days. A notice that the *Client* is not going to pay the *Contractor* the notified sum (and including details required) must be given to the *Contractor* this period of time before the final date for payment.

1.4.1.1 Differences between Option Y(UK)2 and ECC section 5

The certification procedure is unchanged since the ECC requires the payment to be certified within 7 days of the assessment date; and legislation requires the certificate to be issued not later than 5 days after the payment due date (and payment is due 7 days after the assessment date).

Figure 1.3 Times for payment in ECC section 5

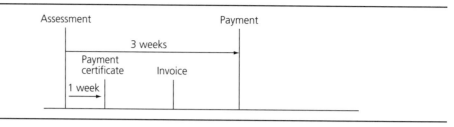

Figure 1.4 Times for payment in Y(UK)2

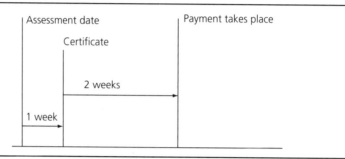

Clause 51.2 requires payment to be made within 3 weeks after the assessment date. The 3-week time period is a default that can be changed using an optional statement in the Contract Data. The important point is that the trigger is the assessment date (Figure 1.3).

Clause 51.2 requires payment to be made within 3 weeks after the assessment date; and clause Y2.2 of Option Y(UK)2 requires the final date for payment to be made 14 days after payment becomes due (payment becomes due 1 week after the assessment date). The time periods therefore equate to the same timeline. Once again, the 3-week time period is a default that can

Figure 1.5 Times for payment in clause 51.2 and Option Y(UK)2

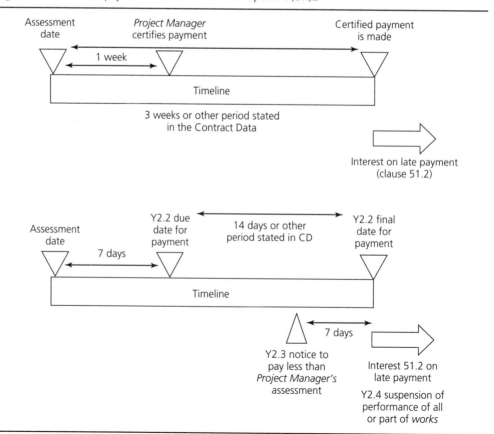

Figure 1.6 Payment procedure with Option Y(UK)2

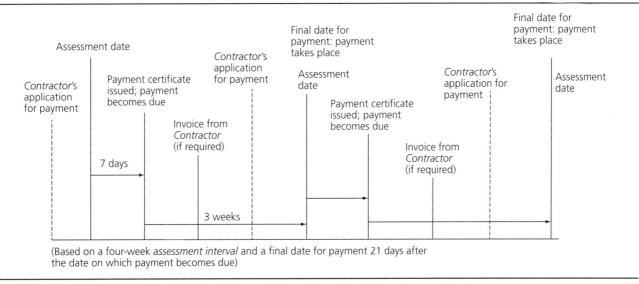

(Based on a four-week *assessment interval* and a final date for payment 21 days after the date on which payment becomes due)

be changed using an optional statement in the Contract Data. This time, however, the trigger is when payment becomes due; that is, certification (Figure 1.4).

There is no difference between the payment date and the final date for payment in Option Y(UK)2. This is because the final date for payment is 14 days after the date on which payment becomes due, whereas in clause 51.2, payment is made 3 weeks after the assessment date (Figure 1.5). Because the date on which payment becomes due is 7 days after the assessment date, the time periods between assessment and payment are the same, although the time periods run from different dates.

1.4.2 The payment procedure with Option Y(UK)2

The payment procedure with Option Y(UK)2 is shown schematically in Figure 1.6.

1.4.3 Intention to pay less with Option Y(UK)2

Option Y(UK)2 includes the concept of paying less than the notified sum to comply with the HGCR Act as amended. If the *Client* intends to pay less than the notified sum to the *Contractor*, then the *Contractor* should be informed about the amount that is to be paid and the basis on which that sum was calculated. The *Client* must tell the *Contractor* this not later than 7 days before the final date for payment (clause Y2.3 of Option Y(UK)2) (see Figure 1.7).

The *Contractor* may suspend performance if the procedure is not followed.

Figure 1.7 The withholding payment procedure

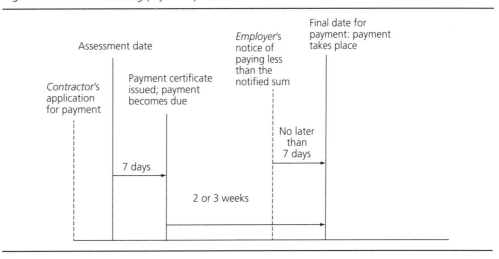

1.5. Assessment at Completion

A specific assessment at Completion is not required in the ECC. Therefore, Completion will be taken account of in the next assessment after Completion has been certified. The Price for Work Done to Date plus other amounts to be paid by the *Contractor* less amounts to be paid by or retained from the *Contractor* will be assessed in the normal way. There could be some differences to take into account secondary Options such as retention (Option X16), delay damages (Option X7) and bonus for early completion (Option X6). There may also be some activities that are assessed at Completion for the sake of convenience rather than because they are wholly chronological activities, such as the submission of building manuals and as-built drawings.

It is possible that a *Contractor* might inform the *Project Manager* that Completion has been achieved, although this is not part of the procedure of the ECC. It is the *Project Manager* who decides that Completion has been achieved, based on the objective criteria stated in the Scope.

1.6. Assessment after termination

Assessments occur at the end of each *assessment interval* until the *Project Manager* issues a termination certificate (clause 50.1). This is in the alternative to Section 1.7 below, as termination is likely to occur before the *defects date* rather than after the *defects date*. The termination procedures in section 9 of the ECC core clauses detail the payments due on termination.

1.7. The payment procedure after the *defects date*

Assessments occur at the end of each *assessment interval* until the *Supervisor* issues the Defects Certificate (clause 50.1).

The Defects Certificate is either a list of Defects that the *Supervisor* has notified before the *defects date* which the *Contractor* has not corrected or, if there are no such Defects, a statement that there are none (clause 11.2(6)). The *Supervisor* issues the Defects Certificate at the *defects date* if there are no notified Defects, or otherwise at the earlier of the end of the last *defect correction period* and the date when all notified Defects have been corrected (clause 44.3). The *defects date* is generally a year or so after Completion takes place, and is identified in Contract Data part one.

This assessment would be related to the release of retention and the deduction of monies where the *Contractor* has not corrected Defects that were required to be corrected.

Therefore, assessments must take place regularly right through the period of the contract from the *starting date* to a date more or less 1 year after Completion was certified.

Managing the Contract
ISBN 978-0-7277-6186-6

http://dx.doi.org/10.1680/mc.61866.015

Chapter 2
Control of time

Synopsis

This chapter discusses aspects relating to the *Contractor's* programme, including

- the terminology used to describe the programme
- what the programme is
- the definition and purpose of the Accepted Programme
- how and when to submit programmes
- what the programme is used for
- what to include in the programme.

2.1. Introduction

One of the underlying principles of the ECC is to avoid and reduce the amount of change that occurs on construction projects. However, the ECC contract recognises that change is inevitable even when the project has been well planned and prepared. Having accepted that change is inevitable, the contract sets out to deal with the effects and consequences of change in an improved way.

The programme is one of the most important tools for use by both the *Contractor* and the *Project Manager* throughout the duration of the project. It is valuable not only as a scheduling tool but also as a pricing and project management tool and a change control tool. Indeed, there is an adage that states that 'planning plus management equals project management'.

The ECC has unique features for dealing with the programme, and is a manual of procedure for the Parties to the contract. The ECC programme is the *Contractor's* programme. The *Contractor* compiles the programme, and they own the terminal float, but the programme is also a project management tool, and there are incentives within the ECC to ensure that the *Contractor* keeps their programme up to date. The programme is used not only as a project planning tool but can also be used for forensic analysis to assess the effects of a compensation event on time and money.

Although the clauses for programming are to be found primarily within section 3 of the ECC core clauses, other clauses might impact or be affected by the programme. The ECC should be read as a whole to be properly understood and implemented.

> The programme is an important tool for use by the *Contractor* and *Project Manager* to manage the contract.

2.2. Terminology

The following words or phrases denote the terminology in the ECC that affects the programme:

- Contract Date   defined in clause 11.2(4)
- *starting date*   identified in Contract Data part one
- *access date*   identified in Contract Data part one
- Completion   defined in clause 11.2(2)
- Completion Date   defined in clause 11.2(3)
- planned Completion   used in clauses 31.2 and 63.5
- Key Date   defined in clause 11.2(11).

2.2.1 The Contract Date

The date when the contract came into existence, and is generally stated in the form of contract/Articles of agreement/letter of award.

2.2.2 The *starting date*

The date stated in the Contract Data part one, when the *Contractor* starts work on the contract.

In effect, the *starting date* is the date from which the *Contractor* is 'on risk' (clause 83.3). The *starting date* is not necessarily the date when the *Contractor* will commence work on Site, since the work commenced at the *starting date* could be design or manufacture required to be undertaken off Site prior to construction or enabling works required on Site.

2.2.3 The *access date(s)*

The date or dates stated in the Contract Data part one, before which the *Contractor* cannot start work on the Site.

The *starting date* is not necessarily the same as the *access date* because the *starting date* is not necessarily the date when the *Contractor* will take access to the Site. This is because, on contracts that have a significant amount of design or manufacturing work for the *Contractor*, the *starting date* could be several weeks or months prior to starting work on Site, to enable the *Contractor* to design or manufacture the Plant and Materials that are required to Provide the Works.

The *Contractor* might not have sole access to the Site. If so, this should be stated in the Scope, as well as any interfaces required.

2.2.4 Completion

Completion is when the *Contractor* has done all the work that the Scope states it is to do by the Completion Date and has corrected notified Defects that would have prevented the *Client* from using the *works* or Others doing their work. This recognises that the *Client* may employ others to undertake works in association with the project and that they may be delayed by uncorrected Defects.

Completion is not a date but a status to be achieved, and the date on which Completion occurs is decided by the *Project Manager* (clause 30.2).

> Completion is not a date.
>
> Completion could occur on the Completion Date, after the Completion Date or before the Completion Date.
>
> The date of Completion is decided by the *Project Manager*.

2.2.5 The Completion Date

The Completion Date is defined in clause 11.2(3), and is the date stated in the Contract Data as the *completion date* unless later changed in accordance with the contract; that is, it is the date on or before which the *Contractor* is contractually obliged to complete the *works* if they are not to be in default.

The Completion Date could be different from the date of Completion, where the date of Completion is that date the *Project Manager* decides the *works* are complete.

2.2.6 Key Dates

A Key Date is the date by which work is to meet the Condition stated in the Contract Data unless the Key Date or Condition is later changed in accordance with the contract (clause 11.2(11)). There is a sanction on the *Contractor* if the work does not meet the Condition stated for a Key Date and the *Client* incurs additional cost as a result (clause 25.3).

2.2.7 Secondary Option X5 – sectional completion

This Option needs to be chosen where the *Client* wishes to take over any part of the *works* before Completion of the whole of the *works*.

2.2.8 Planned Completion

Planned Completion is the date when the *Contractor* plans to complete the *works*. The *Contractor* is required to show both planned Completion and the Completion Date on its programme.

At the outset of the contract, the *Contractor's* planned Completion will be a date earlier than the Completion Date given by the *Client* in Contract Data part one. During the contract, the *Contractor's* planned Completion and the Completion Date will be adjusted. The Completion Date will be adjusted for admissible compensation events, to give a revised Completion Date and the *Contractor's* planned Completion. The *Contractor's* planned Completion will also be adjusted for matters that are at the *Contractor's* risk under the contract. It is therefore possible for the planned Completion to be later than the Completion Date, which may expose the *Contractor* to delay damages.

2.3. What is the programme?

The programme is not a key feature in Joint Contracts Tribunal (JCT) or Institution of Civil Engineers (ICE) contracts. Traditionally, an air of mistrust seems to surround the preparation and review of programmes, with the contractor not wishing to show too much information in the programme for fear that the engineer or architect will manipulate it to their advantage in the event that variations or other changed circumstances arise for additional or reduced works.

With traditional contracts, the contractor is not particularly motivated to prepare and regularly update programmes for joint agreement with the employer's representative, since there are few or no sanctions that can be applied to the contractor apart from warnings that the lack of an approved programme may jeopardise the assessment of claims for extensions of time.

Figure 2.1 A traditional clause 14 programme from the ICE CoC 6th Edition

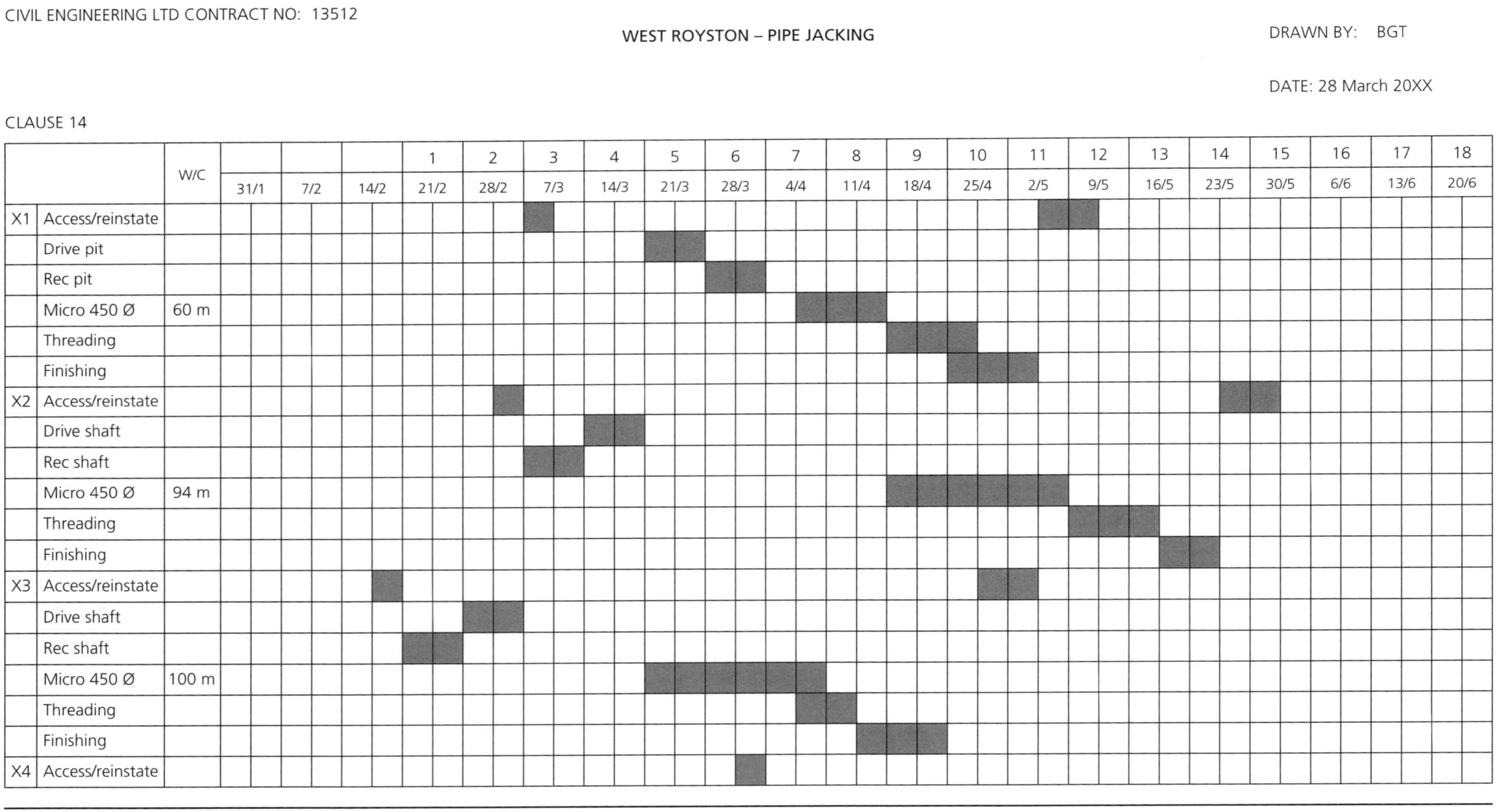

CIVIL ENGINEERING LTD CONTRACT NO: 13512

WEST ROYSTON – PIPE JACKING

DRAWN BY: BGT

DATE: 28 March 20XX

CLAUSE 14

	W/C	31/1	7/2	14/2	1 21/2	2 28/2	3 7/3	4 14/3	5 21/3	6 28/3	7 4/4	8 11/4	9 18/4	10 25/4	11 2/5	12 9/5	13 16/5	14 23/5	15 30/5	16 6/6	17 13/6	18 20/6
X1	Access/reinstate																					
	Drive pit																					
	Rec pit																					
	Micro 450 Ø 60 m																					
	Threading																					
	Finishing																					
X2	Access/reinstate																					
	Drive shaft																					
	Rec shaft																					
	Micro 450 Ø 94 m																					
	Threading																					
	Finishing																					
X3	Access/reinstate																					
	Drive shaft																					
	Rec shaft																					
	Micro 450 Ø 100 m																					
	Threading																					
	Finishing																					
X4	Access/reinstate																					

The fact that the programme may be submitted at the tender stage and is not updated or referred to again in traditional contracts denies the project manager access to a valuable tool.

> The programme is regularly updated, unlike traditional forms of contract.

The programme in the ECC is far more than a simple bar chart showing the intended order and duration of activities to be completed. The programme includes the resources that are used for each activity, including labour and Equipment, and therefore becomes a base comparison for any compensation events. It is a project management tool, and as such is updated regularly.

An example of a traditional clause 14 programme from the ICE Conditions of Contract (CoC) is shown in Figure 2.1. Compare the lack of information in this programme to the requirements of the ECC.

2.4. Definition of the Accepted Programme

The Accepted Programme is the latest programme accepted by the *Project Manager* (clause 11.2(1)).

> The *Project Manager* decides whether to accept a programme submitted by the *Contractor*.

The programme is submitted regularly by the *Contractor* to the *Project Manager* for acceptance, and upon its acceptance it becomes the Accepted Programme. Each subsequent programme submitted by the *Contractor* to the *Project Manager* becomes the Accepted Programme upon acceptance, superseding the previous programme.

2.4.1 When the programme is submitted for acceptance

The *Client* may choose to receive a first programme from the *Contractor* either at the tender stage or after award of the contract:

- Usually the *Client* will request a programme to be submitted by the *Contractor* with their tender in the detail required in clause 31.2. In this instance, the *Client* will not include the optional statement for the programme in Contract Data part one, but will include the optional statement for the programme in Contract Data part two, and the *Contractor* will complete the statement and submit the completed Contract Data part two at the time of tender.

> **Contract Data part two by the *Contractor***
>
> **If a programme is to be identified in the Contract Data**
>
> - The programme identified in the Contract Data is ....
>   [the tenderer inserts the name of the programme here, and includes the programme as part of their tender]

- The alternative is to require the *Contractor* to submit a programme after the start of the contract; that is, within a period of time after the Contract Date identified by the *Client* in Contract Data part one. This alternative is included because it is recognised in the ECC that in certain instances, for example on a cost-reimbursable contract, a fully developed and detailed programme may not be possible prior to the award of the contract. This alternative therefore provides flexibility. In addition, if the *Client* has included a *completion date* and, where required, Conditions and Key Dates, in Contract Data part one, then the *Contractor* is still bound to adhere to these dates, even if the detailed programme is only submitted after the start of the contract.

> **Contract Data part one by the *Client***
>
> **If no programme is identified in part two of the Contract Data**
>
> ■ The period after the Contract Date within which the *Contractor* is to submit a first programme for acceptance is .... [e.g. 2 weeks]

Where possible, however, it is a good policy to have a programme submitted and agreed before contract award as this puts both Parties in a far better position in terms of what is required and when. It also enables the *Client* to ensure that the information and dates stipulated in the invitation to tender have been adhered to. This is particularly relevant for priced contracts. With cost-reimbursable contracts the programme is likely to develop over the course of the project and therefore it may not always be possible for a detailed programme to be submitted at tender stage.

> The *Client* could request a first programme from the *Contractor* either at tender stage or after contract award.

There is, though, a third option to consider: the *Client* could require a detailed programme to be submitted after the Contract Date, but still ask for an outline programme, or perhaps a detailed programme of just one aspect of the *works,* to be submitted as part of the tender, and these can be evaluated by the *Client* and scored without compromising the need for an ECC-compliant programme to be submitted after the Contract Date. In this case, the *Client* would include the relevant statement in Contract Data part one, and the instructions to tenderers would describe the programme to be submitted with the tender.

2.5. The purpose of the Accepted Programme

In keeping with good project management practice, the ECC recognises the programme as being an essential tool for managing the *works*. It enables the *Project Manager* and the *Contractor* to monitor progress and to assess the delaying effects of any compensation events that arise. It also enables the *Project Manager* to see what the time effects will be of a proposed instruction that they might be considering.

It is important always to know what the Completion Date is, if the *Client's* right to delay damages is not to be frustrated. Good programme management by the *Contractor* could protect them from delay damages being levied by the *Client*.

The programme is used for more than just tracking the progress of the project – although this is clearly its primary function.

2.5.1 What the Accepted Programme can be used for

The programme can be used for the following.

2.5.1.1 Resources

The programme includes a statement of how the *Contractor* plans to do the work; that is, a list for each activity of the resources that are intended to be used. Clearly this list will initially be based on the scope of work at the time the programme is drafted – either at the tender stage, or shortly after the start of the contract. This resource statement then becomes useful during the project, as it provides the baseline for how the *Contractor* intends to resource the *works.*

The list of resources for each activity facilitates the estimating of the job by the *Contractor*. Since they will be going through the exercise of forecasting the resources, including the Equipment, used for the job in order to calculate the tender price, this list of resources can be included in the programme, as required by main bullet point 8 of clause 31.2, without further work being required.

> The programme is an essential part of assessing compensation events.

The list of resources also facilitates the assessment of compensation events, both for the *Contractor* and the *Project Manager*. The resources and duration that were expected for the activity can be used as a base when considering the changes as a result of a compensation event. The *Contractor* is able to use those resources estimated in considering the impact of the compensation event, and the *Project Manager* can assess the quotation in the light of the resources estimated originally.

2.5.1.2 Costs

Because of the resources attached to the programme, the costs of the project become clearer, and the *Project Manager* is able to view the programme both from a scheduling point of view and a cost perspective.

This becomes particularly important where the *Project Manager* assesses a compensation event (clause 64), since they will use the tools available to them to do so, and may therefore use the latest Accepted Programme to assess the changes to the Prices as well as the delay to the Completion Date.

2.5.1.3 Project management

The progress of the project is noted on each revised programme so that the *Project Manager* is able to project manage the *works* through the regularly updated programmes by noting whether the project is progressing on time and to budget, using not only the scheduling aspect of the programme but also the resource and cost aspects.

The effect of a compensation event in the programme is more easily assessed since the *Contractor* can immediately see the impact of any delays on their programme. If the *Project Manager* assesses the programme (under clause 64), they will use those tools available to them, including the *Contractor's* programme. If the programme is not up to date, the *Project Manager* could assess the compensation event based entirely on their own experience. The *Contractor* is thus incentivised to keep their programme up to date and accurate.

2.6. What is included in the programme?
2.6.1 All programmes

Each programme that is submitted for acceptance must include the following information (clause 31.2):

- Dates:
  - *starting date*
  - *access dates*
  - Key Dates
  - planned Completion
  - Completion Date
  - dates when the *Contractor* plans to meet each Condition stated for the Key Dates
  - dates when the *Contractor* plans to complete work needed to allow the Client and Others to do their work
  - dates when the *Contractor* will need
    - ○ access (access to a part of the Site if later than its *access date*)
    - ○ acceptances
    - ○ Plant and Materials and other things to be provided by the *Client*
    - ○ information from Others.
- The order and timing of the operations that the *Contractor* plans to do. Operations may be things that the *Contractor* has to undertake in order to do the *work*; for example, the design or manufacture of bathroom pods for hotels that will be manufactured/designed off Site, with the work on Site being their positioning in place by crane and final connections and testing.
- The order and timing of the work of the *Client* and Others as last agreed with them by the *Contractor* or, if not so agreed, as stated in the Scope.
- A statement of how the *Contractor* plans to do the work. See the next item.
- A resource statement: 'for each operation, a statement of how the *Contractor* plans to do the work identifying the principal Equipment and other resources which will be used'.

- Provisions for
  - float
  - time risk allowances
  - health and safety requirements
  - the procedures set out in the contract.
- Other information that the Scope requires the *Contractor* to show in a programme submitted for acceptance.

2.6.2 All programmes except the first programme

In addition to the above information, each revised programme must also include the following information (clause 32.1):

- the actual progress achieved on each operation, and its effect upon the timing of the remaining work
- how the *Contractor* plans to deal with any delays and to correct notified Defects
- any other changes which the *Contractor* proposes to make to the Accepted Programme.

The first bullet point is essential for facilitating the *Project Manager's* reviewing of progress.

The final bullet point is of interest because it allows the *Contractor* to reprogramme *works* to suit any changes they might have with regards to how they will Provide the Works. For example, a *Contractor* could find themselves in a position where they realise that their original planned sequence of operations is no longer realistic or practicable, and they decide to resequence the work. If they do this, and they are at liberty to do so, under Options A and C the revised list of new or amended activities and the programme must correlate. The prices of the individual activities will also need to be amended so that they tie up.

2.6.3 Notes on the programme inclusions
2.6.3.1 The *starting date*, *access dates*, Completion Dates and Key Dates

The *starting date*, *access dates* and Completion Date are all stated in Contract Data part one, and should be included in the programme. The ECC also requires Key Dates to be shown as well as the Condition to be met by each Key Date.

2.6.3.2 Planned Completion

Planned Completion is required to be shown in the programme separately from the Completion Date. Planned Completion shows that date when the *Contractor* is planning to complete the *works*. The date for planned Completion will at the outset of the contract be a date earlier than the Completion Date.

During the contract, however, the *Contractor* may experience problems or encounter risks that are at their risk under the contract, and this may lead to planned Completion being later than the original or adjusted contract Completion Date. In such instances the *Contractor* will be at risk for delay damages, and they will be required to show in revised programmes how they plan to recover the delay.

For the purposes of assessing compensation events, the terminal float (the period between planned Completion in the programme and the Completion Date) is retained by the *Contractor*, as stated in clause 63.5 (delays to Key Dates are assessed on the same basis), where any delay to the Completion Date due to a compensation event is assessed as the length of time that planned Completion is later than planned Completion on the Accepted Programme that is current at the time.

However, even now that there is a facility for planning to complete earlier than the Completion Date stated in the contract, few *Contractors* appear to be including a planned Completion Date in their programme.

It should also be pointed out that the Completion Date for the contract is something different from Completion. Completion is a status (for more information, see Chapter 1 of Book One is this series) that is achieved when the *Contractor* has fulfilled their duties as described in the contract. Completion could therefore be achieved on, before or after the Completion Date.

The ECC includes the concept of Key Dates (which are defined in clause 11.2(11) as 'the date by which work is to meet the Condition stated') and states in clause 63.5: 'A delay to a Key Date is assessed as the length of time that, due to the compensation event, the planned date when the Condition stated for a Key Date will be met is later than the date shown on the Accepted Programme current at the dividing date'.

In addition, the *Contractor* must make sure that any changes to their methods of working do not affect the correlation of the Accepted Programme and the Activity Schedule in an Option A contract.

In the ECC, the wording of clause A55.3 reads as follows:

'If the *Contractor*

- changes a planned method of working at its discretion so that the activities on the Activity Schedule do not relate to the operations on the Accepted Programme or
- corrects the Activity Schedule so that the activities on the Activity Schedule relate to the Scope

the *Contractor* submits a revision of the Activity Schedule to the *Project Manager* for acceptance.'

2.6.3.3 Other dates to be shown on the Programme

It is important for the *Client* to advise the *Contractor* of the dates when they require the *Contractor* to complete particular works (but for **use not take over**, i.e. not a *section* of the *works*) or the degree to which they need it to be completed to enable the *Client* and Others, whose names or allocations must also be included in the documents, to do their work.

An example may be a statement such as:

The *Contractor* shall complete the proposed new road between chainages 0 to 100 m by the 10th December 20XX to allow access for the *Client* to the existing warehouse adjacent to the new road. It is a requirement that the road be complete up to base course level with all adjacent kerbs, drainage and street lighting.

The statement needs to be clear and unambiguous: the *Contractor* should not be in any doubt as to what it is they have to do by the key date (the term Key Date(s) is a defined term, and the *Client* identifies the condition of work to be completed by the *key date* in the Contract Data). In the ECC, the box above is an example of the *condition* of work to be completed by a *key date*.

2.6.3.4 Access to a part of a Site if later than its *access date*

The importance of this is that the Contract Data part one should include the dates when the *Client* can give access to parts of the Site.

The *access dates* are

	part of the Site	date
(1)	....	....
(2)	....	....
(3)	....	....

These dates have to be shown on the *Contractor's* programme. If the *Contractor* decides that they do not need to access a part of the Site on the *access dates* given, then they can decide to include a later access date in their programme. The *Client's* contractual obligation is to give access changes to this later date shown on the *Contractor's* programme.

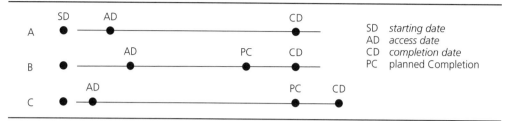

Figure 2.2 Access dates

Figure 2.2 shows in a simple form the consequences of giving a later *access date* than that given in Contract Data part one. Line A shows the dates for the *starting date*, *access date* and *completion date*, all of which are provided by the *Client* in Contract Data part one and all of which the *Contractor* must show on their programme. Line B shows the Contract Data part one *starting date* and *completion date* on the *Contractor's* programme. The *Contractor's* programme also shows the date on which they need access to the Site, as it is later that the *access date*, and their planned Completion that they are obliged to include in the programme.

As the access date in Line B is a later date than in Line A, that date becomes the contractual date for access.

Line C shows an *access date* earlier than the *access date* given in the Contract Data and a Completion Date later than that given in the Contract Data. The *Project Manager* will not accept this programme because it does not show the information that this contract requires, and because it does not allow the *Client*, other contractors and Others to start, carry out and complete their works as they intended and as stated in the Scope.

2.6.3.5 Acceptances

If the *Contractor* is designing part or the whole of the *works*, then the *Contractor* will need to show in its programme the dates when it requires its *Contractor* design to be accepted by the *Project Manager*, which includes both permanent and temporary works.

In some instances the Scope may contain a requirement for the *Contractor* to submit particulars of the design of an item of Equipment (temporary shoring to a building façade, crash deck, etc.). The *Client* may feel that it is wise to do this because the failure of such Equipment may potentially pose a significant health, security, safety, operational, environmental, public or people fatality risk.

In such instances the *Client* will wish to demonstrate that if such failure occurs they acted in a manner that mitigated or reduced such risks. The *Project Manager* may also (clause 23.1) instruct the *Contractor* to submit particulars of their design of Equipment during the contract. Again, in such an instance this will need to be shown in any revised programmes submitted by the *Contractor* for acceptance by the *Project Manager*.

On some projects the acceptances given by the *Client* will need to be approved by third parties – for example, the utilities or statutory bodies. In these instances the *Client* needs to ensure that they have adequate time allowances built into the acceptance system for *Contractor*-designed work. It also needs to be clear in the Scope who has the responsibility to liaise and interface with such third parties.

2.6.3.6 Plant and Materials and other things

The *Contractor* must show in their programme the dates when they require Plant and Materials which the Scope states the *Client* is to provide.

This will cover situations where the *Client* might be a company that has items such as standard fittings or furnishings that they have for all their stores, factories or facilities. In some instances, the Plant and Materials will be available or will be provided from the *Client's* own stores.

A practical example of this is where the *Client* has placed a contract with a *Contractor* to carry out some utility diversion work. In order for the overall programme for the *works* to be achieved, it was necessary for the *Client* to pre-order the pipework and fittings because they are on a long lead-in time to purchase of 18 weeks.

The Scope should also state a date after which the *Client*-supplied materials will be available for call-off by the *Contractor*.

2.6.3.7 The order and timing of the *Contractor's* work

The 'operations' referred to in clause 31.2 do not necessarily equate to an *activity schedule* or *bill of quantities* item, as there may be several operations to such an item. For example, there may be an item in the *activity schedule* that reads as follows:

Activity No.	Description	Price
300	Foundations up to DPC Level	£25 000

This one activity has several operations:

1 excavate for strip foundations
2 earthwork support
3 dispose of excavated material
4 level and compact bottom of excavations
5 concrete strip foundations
6 brickwork, including damp proof course (DPC) and cavity fill
7 backfilling, including level and compact.

In this example, the *Contractor* must show in their programme the order and timing of all the operations that the *Contractor* plans to do to Provide the Works, and not just the headline activity – Foundations up to DPC Level – as well as the information that shows how each activity on the *activity schedule* relates to the operations in each programme submitted (clause A31.4).

Compatibility of the *activity schedule* and the Accepted Programme

It is essential that the *activity schedule* and the Accepted Programme correlate and that each has the same list of activities.

The *Contractor* must provide information that shows how each activity on the *activity schedule* relates to the operations in each programme that the *Contractor* submits for acceptance.

If the documents received from the *Contractor* are not compatible, then they should be made to be so. Clause A55.3 requires that where a *Contractor* changes a planned method of working at their discretion so that the *activity schedule* does not comply with the Accepted Programme, it submits a revision of the *activity schedule* to the *Project Manager* for acceptance.

Incompatibility is a reason for the *Project Manager* not accepting the programme (the programme does not show the information that the contract requires).

If the documents do not correlate, then it will be impossible to monitor the true effects that compensation events will have (or have had) upon the Accepted Programme, and hence the time aspects of the project will not be manageable.

2.6.3.8 The order and timing of the *Client's* part of the *works*

The *Client* needs to ensure that any constraints on how the *Contractor* Provides the Works are stated in the Scope. The *Contractor* will then need to reflect these constraints in their planning of the order and timing of the *works*.

To introduce constraints at a later date once work has commenced would be a change to the Scope, and consequently a compensation event.

The same rule applies for

■ any work that the *Client* is to carry out
■ any work to be undertaken by Others
■ Key Dates (a defined term – see clause 11.2(11)) by which the *Client* or Others need to complete their work.

This emphasises the requirement for the *Client* to provide precise and accurate information.

2.6.3.9 The importance of dates in the programme

The *Contractor's* programme is required to show not only the order and timing of their own work but also that of the *Client* and Others, and the dates when the *Contractor* needs access, acceptances and things to be provided by the *Client*. This allows the *Contractor* to plan their operations and to be proactive in their requirements. It enables the *Contractor* to assess any impact on the programme of the *Client* not doing their work, or not providing something for any resulting compensation event.

The dates to be included in the programme (e.g. dates when the *Contractor* plans to complete work to allow the *Client* and Others to do their work and dates when the *Contractor* will need access, acceptances and things provided by the *Client*) become more important if a compensation event arises.

Because one of the important aspects of the programme is that it provides forensic evidence, the *Contractor* can use the programme to prove delays. They can only do this, however, if the dates when they required things were included in the programme.

> The programme can help both the *Client* and the *Contractor* in assessing compensation events.
>
> The programme enables the *Client* to carry out what-if scenarios.

Several of the compensation events listed in clause 60.1 relate back to the programme and the information that the *Contractor* has included in the programme. For example, the following are compensation events:

- The *Client* does not allow access by the later of an *access date* and the date for access required by the Accepted Programme (clause 60.1(2)). This relates back to the programme requirements for the *Contractor* to show
  - *access dates* (the date when the *Client* is allowing the *Contractor* access to and use of the Site)
  - the dates when they will need access to a Site if it is later than the *access date*.

Since the *access dates* are included in the Contract Data, the non-inclusion of those dates in the programme will not necessarily result in the *Contractor* being denied this compensation event. Similarly, if access is required later than the *access date*, non-inclusion of this date will also not necessarily affect the *Contractor's* right to the compensation event, since the trigger could still be the *access date* as stated in the Contract Data.

- The *Client* does not provide something, which it is to provide by the date shown in the Accepted Programme (clause 60.1(3)). This relates back to the programme requirements for the *Contractor* to show the dates when the *Contractor* will need Plant and Materials and other things to be provided by the *Client*.

The obvious question to ask is what happens if the *Client* is to provide things to the *Contractor* but the *Contractor* has failed to include these elements in the programme? Clearly, if the *Client* fulfils their obligations, there will be no repercussions. If, however, the *Client* is late in their provision of an item, and the *Contractor* wishes to claim compensation, the event is not a compensation event because the *Contractor* has not fulfilled their obligations in including the dates in their programme. It appears that such neglect on the part of the *Contractor* is not envisaged by the contract, since the contract probably expects the *Contractor* to do whatever is within their power to complete the contract successfully. It may be interpreted that the *Contractor* has no recourse under the contract. However, it is likely that the *Client's* failure and the *Contractor's* failure do not make it right to deprive the *Contractor*, when it would not be justified. The *Contractor* may be able to produce a forensic analysis of their programme, working backwards in time to show when they would have expected the *Client's* item in order to carry out succeeding operations.

However, it would be much simpler, less expensive, more effective and more co-operative just to include the information and dates in the programme.

■ The *Client* or Others do not work within the times shown on the Accepted Programme (clause 60.1(5)). This relates back to the programme requirements for the *Contractor* to show

– the order and timing of the work of the *Client* and Others either as stated in the Scope or as last agreed with them by the *Contractor*.

The comments for the previous compensation event apply here as well.

All these elements of the programme emphasise the importance of the programme for the *Contractor* and for the mutual operations of the Parties. The proper and full drafting of the programme affects the smooth running of the project and the *Contractor's* ability to notify compensation events and maintain their profit.

> The programme is an essential part of assessing compensation events.

2.6.3.10 Statements of how the *Contractor* plans to do the work

When the contract talks about the programme, it includes method statements; therefore, each activity that may have several operations will require several method statements. Although the ECC refers to 'a statement of how the *Contractor* plans to do the work identifying the principal Equipment and other resources which will be used' (clause 31.2), this book refers to a method statement and a resource statement throughout, for ease of reference.

It should also be noted that the activities on the Option A *activity schedule* should relate to the operations of each programme.

> Statements 'of how the *Contractor* plans to do the work' are part of the programme.

When to call for a statement of how the *Contractor* plans to do the work and the like
Section 3 of the core clauses of the *conditions of contract* requires the *Contractor* to submit a great deal of information. It then becomes a management exercise to decide when to call for the information that supports the Accepted Programme, taking into account the main Option applicable to the contract.

On large projects, it may be impractical to call for all the method statements at the beginning of the project, and a systematic approach to the submission and acceptance of method statements should be set up that allows adequate time for all the documentation to go through the *Client's* and *Contractor's* quality systems.

On small projects, it might be quite feasible to have all the information required submitted at the beginning of the project, perhaps prior to work commencing on Site.

2.6.3.11 The resource statement

The resource statement is something other than a method statement (which is also required with the programme) although it could be included in it as envisaged by clause 31.2. The resource statement is a description of the resources that the *Contractor* intends to use for each activity, such as labour and Equipment. It is a part of the programme, and is incorporated into the programme and is therefore required with every programme submitted, including those submitted as part of a quotation for a compensation event.

A resource statement could help the *Contractor* in their pricing, particularly if Option A (which uses an *activity schedule*) is the chosen pricing mechanism. Including the method and the resources required for each operation also allows the *Contractor* to plan their resources effectively and to be proactive in their procurement of those resources. Lastly, the effect of a compensation event on the programme is more easily assessed since the *Contractor* can immediately see the impact of any delays on their programme. If the *Project Manager* assesses the programme (clause 64), they will use those tools available to them, including the *Contractor's* programme. If the programme is not up to date, the *Project Manager* may assess the compensation event based entirely on their own experience. The *Contractor* is thus incentivised to keep their programme up to date and accurate.

For operation 300(i), a resource statement might read as follows:

Activity No.   **Description**

300   Foundations up to DPC Level

Schedule of Equipment and other resources

- JCT 3XC driver
- 3T dumper driver
- Excavation gang
- 1 ganger
- 2 labourers

2.6.3.12 Float

It should be noted that the *Contractor* is required to show float and time risk allowances. Once these elements have been accepted by the *Project Manager* and incorporated into the Accepted Programme, they would tend to remain for the duration of the project.

There are a number of different types of float in programming. There is 'free' float between non-critical activities, 'total float', which is float on an activity, and 'terminal float', which is any float that exists between planned Completion and the Completion Date.

- Free float   The amount of time a task/operation can be delayed before affecting any other task.
- Total float   The amount of time a task can be delayed without affecting planned Completion or reducing the terminal float (where this has been examined by the *Project Manager* and accepted as realistic).
- Terminal float   Float attached to the whole programme and to sectional Completion (i.e. any float between planned Completion and the Completion Date).

The ECC clears up the old argument about 'entitlement', in that the terminal float belongs to the *Contractor*. Free float and total float are available to accommodate the time effects of compensation events in order to mitigate or avoid any delay to planned Completion, and could therefore be said to belong to the *Client*. Time entitlement is also based upon entitlement, and not need as it is with traditional contracts, such as the ICE and JCT contracts.

The *Contractor* owns the terminal float.

The assessment of time is based upon entitlement, not need.

Therefore, any compensation event that delays any activity on the critical path (i.e. an activity with zero float) must as a consequence delay planned Completion, giving rise to a commensurate delay to the Completion Date.

Let us run through an example. Figure 2.3 shows an outline programme for a project. The critical activities are shown by open boxes, and the non-critical by solid boxes. It can be seen from the diagram that the time between the planned Completion and the Completion Date is called the 'terminal float', and this float belongs to the *Contractor*.

2.6.3.13 Time risk allowances

The *Contractor* is required to show time risk allowances in their programme. Once they have been accepted by the *Project Manager* and incorporated into the Accepted Programme, they would tend to remain for the duration of the project. Time risk allowances are owned by the *Contractor* as part of their realistic planning (note the phraseology, which relates directly back

Figure 2.3 Assessment of the time effects of change

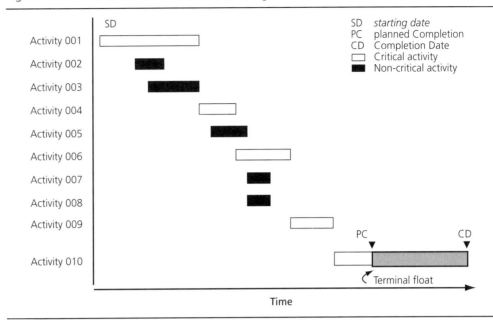

to one of the *Project Manager's* reasons for non-acceptance of the programme in clause 31.3) to cover their risk.

An example of this is the allowance that the *Contractor* builds into their programme for down time occurring due to undertaking earthworks during the winter. The allowances should either be clearly identified in the programme as allowances, or be included in the time periods allocated to the specific activities.

2.6.3.14 Health and safety requirements

Some *Clients* might have additional health and safety requirements (clause 27.4) that impact on the *Contractor's* programme. These kinds of requirements should be clearly laid out in the Scope and incorporated by the *Contractor* into their programme.

The *Contractor* should be able to demonstrate any allowances that they have made in their programme for health and safety requirements. An example of this is time allowances for workmen to prepare themselves at the beginning of a shift and for washing themselves down and cleaning equipment when removing blue asbestos, which necessitates 'decontamination zones', 'sealed areas' and so on.

The Construction (Design and Management) Regulations 2015 underline that this is a very important and serious consideration for the *Contractor*, who in the case of an accident might have to demonstrate to the Health and Safety Executive that they had allowed adequate time to undertake the work safely.

In some instances, it may be difficult to show the allowances made in the programme. However, it is not impossible. Depending on the type of planning software used and the competence of the user of the planning tool, planners can produce programmes that can be very detailed, showing time-risk allowances, float, critical path and so on. These programmes can then be rolled up into a higher-level programme.

Where the use of the more sophisticated planning tools are felt not to be appropriate, then in these instances the contract intends that these allowances should be shown in the statements of how the *Contractor* plans to do the work and that are part of the programme in the contract.

2.6.3.15 Procedures set out in the contract

This is a bit vague for the ECC but is probably unavoidable in that the contract cannot cover all the possible alternatives. It is therefore very important for the drafters of the documents to ensure that they clearly and concisely spell out any other special requirements they have in the Scope.

It is also highlighting the need to recognise such things as the *period for reply*, and is consequently warning the *Contractor* to allow for such things in the programme as the period that the *Project Manager* has for accepting *Contractor* designs.

2.6.3.16 Other information required by the Scope

Other information is a very broad area, and it is important that the *Client* states in the Scope any information they want to see, bearing in mind that the Scope is not only the information included in the said document but could also be an instruction given to the *Contractor* in accordance with the contract (clause 11.2(16)).

For example, this could cover

- dates when, in order to Provide the Works, the *Contractor* is planning to obtain consents or
- dates when they are planning to submit any design to the *Project Manager* for acceptance.

This information can be useful to the *Project Manager* in planning when they need particular resources available, such as designers.

It could also cover the dates when the *Contractor* needs the completed Scope. This will cover situations where the *Client* has been unable to complete all the Scope required by the *Contractor* in order for them to Provide the Works. This type of situation might occur where the *Client* wishes to start a project quickly and has been unable to complete certain elements of the Scope – items such as consents or approvals. In such instances, the *Client* should include assumptions within the Scope.

Information release schedules should be included in the Scope, and the *Contractor* should be required to reflect in their first programme for acceptance the dates contained on the schedule. This way, as long as the *Client* meets the dates, there will be no case for a delay to the Completion Date (unless of course the information is **different** from that assumed).

2.6.3.17 Actual progress

In addition to the items required by clause 31, clause 32 requires the *Contractor* to include other items into their revised programme, such as actual progress and its effect on the remaining work, delays and notified Defects. In this way, the *Project Manager* is aware of whether the project is on time and, to a certain extent, on budget, and the *Contractor* is able to plan their programme and resources based around contractual events. The Accepted Programme forms the as-built programme as time goes by, so that forensic analysis is facilitated through the resources and timing available in the programme.

2.7. Submission of the first programme

The ECC requires a first programme to be submitted by the *Contractor* to the *Project Manager* for acceptance either at the tender stage (where the optional statement is included in Contract Data part two) or shortly after the start of the contract (where the optional statement is included in Contract Data part one) – see the discussion in Section 2.4.1 of this book. Once the programme has been accepted, it becomes the Accepted Programme, and both Parties work from this programme until the next programme is accepted and becomes the Accepted Programme.

> The first programme is submitted with the tender or within a stipulated time (e.g. 4 weeks) after the award of the contract.

If the *Contractor* does not submit their first programme within the time required, the *Project Manager* retains 25% (clause 50.5) of the Price for Work Done to Date to the *Contractor* until the first programme has been submitted (note that it is the submission of the programme that is important, not the acceptance of the programme by the *Project Manager*). This is clearly a powerful incentive to the *Contractor*, and emphasises the importance attached to the programme by the ECC. Many employers prefer to see a programme with the tender submitted.

> The *Project Manager* may withhold a quarter of monies due (Price For Work Done To Date) if the *Contractor* does not submit a first programme.

A further note regarding the retention of the amount is that, as with other aspects of payment, such as delay damages, the retention of monies in this vein is not an option that may be exercised by the *Client*. It is an obligation of the *Project Manager* to carry out their actions under the contract and to retain the 25%. They are not given the choice by the use of the word 'may'.

For some of the main Options in the ECC, the requirement to submit a programme with the tender may not be as informative as the *Client* would like it to be, particularly where information is minimal or where both Parties know that the information will be changing as drawings are amended or as other information is revealed. Some companies still refer to a programme submitted with the tender as the 'tender programme' and a revised programme submitted after the contract as the 'contract programme'. The ECC does not recognise this kind of terminology, which tends to imply that the tender programme is of less importance than the contract programme, whereas in the ECC, once accepted, each programme is important.

2.8. How often is the programme revised?

The *Contractor* submits a revised programme to the *Project Manager* for acceptance on four different occasions:

- **Every regular period during the contract** (clause 32.2). Contract Data part one dictates the period within which the programme has to be revised. This could be 4 weeks or 8 weeks, or even 3 months, depending on the complexity and length of the project. Some *Project Managers* even ask for two different types of programme, one of which is more complex and is to be submitted less frequently. Some *Project Managers* also require a summary programme at weekly progress meetings. Although this will clearly be based on the Accepted Programme, its requirement is more likely to be described in the Scope.

> The *Contractor* updates the programme regularly.

It is recommended that *Project Managers* take heed of the complexity and duration of the project in deciding how frequently they wish to see the programme. Although the programme is a pivotal project management tool, it can also be an onerous and possibly expensive document for the *Contractor* to produce, and *Project Managers* should try to avoid making the task more difficult for *Contractors* in requesting very frequent revisions unnecessarily.
- **If they choose to do so** (clause 32.2). The *Contractor* may choose to submit a programme for acceptance to the *Project Manager* outwith the obligatory regular period. An example is where they have amended sequencing or they have changed the method or resourcing of an activity. The *Project Manager* is obliged to reply to the *Contractor* with their acceptance or otherwise of the programme within 2 weeks of the *Contractor* having submitted it.
- **When they have been instructed to do so by the *Project Manager*** (clause 32.2). If the *Project Manager* instructs the *Contractor* to submit a revised programme for acceptance, the *Contractor* is obliged to submit the programme within the *period for reply*.
- **If a compensation event has affected the programme** (clause 62.2). A quotation for a compensation event comprises changes to the Prices and a delay to the Completion Date. Where the compensation event has had (or will have) the effect of changing the programme, then the *Contractor* has to submit a revised programme with their quotation showing the alterations to the Accepted Programme. If the programme is affected simply because a statement of how the *Contractor* plans to do the work or resourcing changes, but the Completion Date remains the same, a revised programme still has to be submitted since both the resources and the method are a part of the programme. The time periods for the submission are as described in the compensation event procedure, but, in general, the *Contractor* has 3 weeks to submit a quotation from being instructed to do so (clause 62.3). Note that if the *Contractor* does not submit a revised programme

with a compensation event quotation as required, the *Project Manager* may make their own assessment of the compensation event (clause 64.1).

2.9. Acceptance of the programme

The *Project Manager* may accept or not accept the first programme and each subsequent programme submitted for acceptance by the *Contractor* based on various criteria stated in the contract. It is only when a programme is accepted that it becomes the Accepted Programme.

> If the *Project Manager* does not accept the programme for any reason other than the four stated in clause 31.3, it is a compensation event (clause 60.1(9)).

Note that if there is no Accepted Programme – that is, if the first programme submitted by the *Contractor* has not been accepted – the *Project Manager* may use their own assessment of the programme for work that is affected by a compensation event (clause 64.2). The *Project Manager* may do the same if the *Contractor* has not submitted a revised programme (or alterations to a programme) for acceptance as required by the contract.

2.9.1 Reasons for non-acceptance

There are only four reasons for the *Project Manager* to refuse acceptance of the programme. They are as follows (clause 31.3):

- the *Contractor's* plans that it shows are not practicable
- it does not show the information that the contract requires
- it does not represent the *Contractor's* plans realistically
- it does not comply with the Scope.

Although in general the clauses of the contract are very clear, it would be fair to say that one or two of the above reasons for refusing acceptance of a programme could be interpreted in various ways. In particular, realistic or practicable planning tends to be subjective, and therefore any non-acceptances based on these reasons should be carefully considered. The following subsections discuss the reasons in more detail.

2.9.1.1 The *Contractor's* plans in the programme are not practicable

The first reason refers to the *Contractor's* plans only. An example is where the *Contractor's* programme shows their planned progress on a tunnel to be 90 m/week. The *Contractor's* original accepted programme shows them achieving 10 m/week, and their actual rate of progress is 50 m/week. The best output ever achieved by a *Contractor* on a tunnel of this type under similar conditions is 75 m/week. The *Contractor's* plans are therefore not realistic.

When assessing tender submissions, data relating to output rates/production rates may be very useful to benchmark the tenders received.

2.9.1.2 The programme does not show information that the contract requires

The second reason refers to the contract, and it should be noted that references to the contract include not only the ECC *conditions of contract* but also the Scope and whatever other information and documentation has been incorporated into the contract. An example of this is where the programme does not show the *access date* or sectional Completion Dates.

Can the *Project Manager* refuse to accept a programme because the Completion Date shown in the submitted programme is later than the Completion Date shown in the Accepted Programme, but there is no compensation event or other reason for the date to have been delayed? One could argue that the reason for non-acceptance of 'does not show information that this contract requires' could apply, since the contract requires the Completion Date to be shown, whereas the date shown as the Completion Date in the programme is not the Completion Date. The same reason could be argued where the actual progress has not been measured accurately against planned progress in the programme.

2.9.1.3 The programme does not represent the *Contractor's* plans realistically

An example of the third reason is where a *Contractor's* programme assumes use of driven piles and the *Project Manager* is aware that the Site team is using bored piles.

Figure 2.4 Secant piled lift shaft box

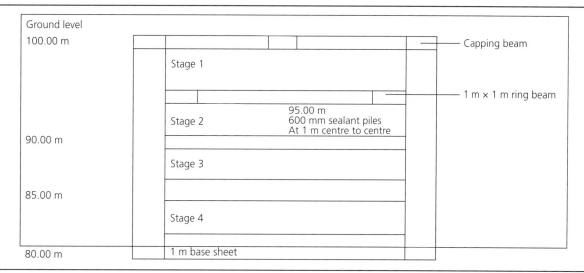

Another example is where a *Contractor's* programme shows commissioning/testing a bank of six lifts at the same time, requiring **all** the available commissioning engineers to be used at one time.

2.9.1.4 The programme does not comply with the Scope

An example of the fourth reason is that the programme has not taken into account any design constraints stated in the Scope. An illustration of this could be where the *Contractor* cannot undertake a certain item of the *works* until certain other things have been completed.

Let us say that a new secant piled lift shaft box is to be constructed top down (Figure 2.4). The Scope might stipulate that the lift shaft box is to be constructed top down in a series of stages as follows:

Stage 1: level 100.00 to 95.00 m
Stage 2: level 95.00 to 90.00 m
Stage 3: level 90.00 to 85.00 m
Stage 4: level 85.00 to 80.00 m.

No excavation work can commence until the previous stage is complete and the 1 × 1 m concrete ring beam at each level has been left to cure for a minimum of 14 days after the last concrete pour.

If the *Contractor* shows an activity in their programme allowing only 7 days for curing before excavating the next level, then the work is not in accordance with the Scope.

2.9.2 Resubmission of an unaccepted programme

If the *Project Manager* does not accept a programme, the *Contractor* is obliged to resubmit the programme within the *period for reply* (clauses 13.4 and 32.2). Once the *Contractor* receives notification of non-acceptance, they should automatically set about drafting a revised programme for submission to the *Project Manager*.

2.9.3 Timing of the acceptance or non-acceptance

The *Project Manager* has 2 weeks to reply to the *Contractor* after the *Contractor* submitted their programme for acceptance.

If the *Project Manager* does not reply within the allotted timescale, then the *Contractor* may choose to notify the *Project Manager* that it [the *Contractor*] has not received a reply within the required 2 weeks. If the *Project Manager* has still not replied within a further 1 week, then the *Contractor* can safely assume that their submitted programme has been accepted.

In addition, it is a compensation event (clause 60.1(6)) if the *Project Manager* does not reply to a communication within the time period stated in the contract. The *Contractor* therefore becomes entitled to an assessment of time and money for the *Project Manager's* tardiness. This sanction for a late reply reinforces the view that a non-reply is deemed to be acceptance.

2.10. Completion

The *Contractor* is required to Provide the Works so that Completion is on or before the Completion Date (clause 30.1). Time is therefore of the essence in ECC contracts.

Completion takes place when the *Project Manager* decides that Completion has been achieved (clause 30.2). This could be on, before or after the Completion Date. The *Contractor* is not required to notify the *Project Manager* that they consider the *works* to be complete. The *Project Manager* need not take heed of any such notice that the *Contractor* chooses to submit. The *Project Manager* would clearly take into account the details in the Scope about when Completion takes place. In addition, Completion cannot take place if there are still uncorrected Defects that would prevent the *Client* from using the *works* and Others from doing their work (clause 11.2(2)).

The *Project Manager* is required to certify Completion within 1 week after they decide that Completion has taken place.

2.10.1 Take over and Completion

Take over and Completion are linked by time and circumstance. Take over generally follows Completion; however, sometimes take over could occur before Completion. The ECC details the procedures to be followed in all cases.

2.10.1.1 Take over before Completion

If the *Client* starts to use any part of the *works* before Completion has been certified, then it is deemed to have taken over the *works*. The exception to this is where the take over has occurred because of a reason stated in the Scope or to suit the *Contractor's* method of working (clause 35.2).

2.10.1.2 Take over after Completion

The *Client* takes over the *works* not more than 2 weeks after Completion (clause 35.1).

Note that the *Client* need not take over the *works* before the Completion Date if they have stated in the Contract Data that they are unwilling to do so. This is different from taking over before Completion. The former case refers to the situation where the *Contractor* has completed the *works* before the Completion Date stated in the contract, but the *Client* is not willing to take over the *works* earlier than they would have if the *Contractor* had completed on time.

2.11. Take over by the *Client*
2.11.1 How it happens

'Taking over' is the term used by the ECC to signify that the *Client* has taken over the *works* or a part thereof.

The *Project Manager* certifies take over of any part of the *works* within 1 week of the date of take over (clause 35.3).

2.11.2 What it means

Take over means that access to the Site or part thereof returns to the *Client*. The *Contractor* no longer has a right to access the Site, and the *Client* has to make arrangement for access for the *Contractor* in order for them to correct Defects that occur.

It also signifies a risk transfer in terms of liability for loss/damage to the *works* from the *Contractor* to the *Client*.

2.12. Acceleration

Acceleration under the ECC deserves a special mention because it is treated differently from traditional contracts.

Acceleration is described in the contract as being an instruction from the *Project Manager* to achieve Completion before the Completion Date. This description of acceleration is not requesting the *Contractor* to speed up their progress in order to achieve Completion on the Completion Date, which is something else entirely.

Acceleration is a useful provision for those clients for whom time is critical. For example, retail companies have critical times such as Easter and Christmas, on which they might wish or need to be open.

The price to the *Client* for achieving acceleration is whatever the *Contractor* chooses to quote to the *Client* (clause 36.1). Acceleration is not a compensation event, and therefore the basis of the quotation does not have to be the Defined Cost.

Clause 36 allows both the *Contractor* and the *Project Manager* to propose an acceleration to achieve Completion before the Completion Date, and the procedure only goes ahead if both of them are prepared to consider the proposed change.

If both are prepared to consider the proposed change, then the *Project Manager* instructs the *Contractor* to submit a quotation, and the *Contractor* must do so within 3 weeks of the instruction.

> The *Contractor* is not obliged to accelerate.

There is an alternative way of maintaining the Completion Date when changes occur to affect the programme. In the compensation event procedure, the *Project Manager* may instruct the *Contractor* to submit alternative quotations based on different ways of dealing with the compensation event, after discussing with the *Contractor* different ways of dealing with the compensation event that are practicable. If the *Project Manager* wishes to maintain the Completion Date despite a compensation event that could have delayed the Completion Date, they could instruct the *Contractor* to submit an alternative quotation maintaining the Completion Date. This could involve overtime or a change to the sequencing of the programme, or both, and is likely to cost more than a simple change to the Prices combined with a delay to the Completion Date. In any case, the *Project Manager* then has the choice of quotations.

2.13. Other aspects of programming in the ECC
2.13.1 The *Contractor's* programme

It is important to understand that the programme is the *Contractor's* programme. The *Project Manager* does not have the same powers to amend the programme as in traditional contracts. There is no statement in the ECC that the *Contractor* must use best endeavours to progress the *works*, nor does the *Project Manager* have the ability to instruct the *Contractor* to speed up their progress to ensure that Completion is on or before the Completion Date.

If the *Contractor's* actual progress is lagging behind their planned progress, there is not much that the *Project Manager* can do to encourage the *Contractor* to complete on time other than instruct the submission of another programme. This probably works on the assumption of mutual trust and co-operation and also that it is not really in the *Contractor's* interests to work slowly since (depending on the payment option) this could cost the *Contractor* money, especially if Option X7 (delay damages) has been selected.

The *Project Manager* has the choice of not accepting a subsequent programme if it does not show the *Contractor's* plans realistically (where the programme still shows progress on schedule) but this does not necessarily achieve what the *Project Manager* really wants, which is for the *Contractor* to speed up (as opposed to accelerate).

Some employers therefore include in the contract that the *Project Manager* may instruct the *Contractor* to speed up their progress. If the payment Option is C, D or E, the *Client* might even include the cost of this speeding up as a Disallowed Cost (by amending the Disallowed Cost definition in clause 11.2(26).

2.13.2 The *Client's* programme

Some *Clients* call the master plan or schedule that they have drafted the 'programme', and the *Contractor* is expected to conform to the *Client's* programme.

This is all very well, but it is unlikely that the *Client's* programme includes all the aspects of the programme as described above and that the *Contractor* is obliged to include in their programme. The *Contractor* might buy into the *Client's* programme as the master programme for the overall project, but would be obliged under the contract to produce their own programme that would provide for their notifying compensation events and would provide the information that the *Project Manager* needs in order to manage the project effectively.

The above also applies to Subcontractors when working for *Contractors*.

2.13.3 The programme affecting cash flow

The programme may affect the cash flow, particularly for Option A contracts, where the *Contractor* is not paid for an activity until they have completed that activity. The *Contractor* therefore needs to ensure that the activities described in the programme can be completed before an assessment date (see Chapter 2, section 2.4.1.3, in Book Two of this series; clause A11.2(29), so that they (the *Contractor*) are always assured of completed activities and therefore payments.

The problem is that the shorter the activities, the more opportunity there is for Completion of those activities and therefore payment, but the longer it takes to produce the programme. The *Contractor* should therefore try to reach a balance between the length of the activities and the need for cash flow.

2.13.4 A moving target

The Accepted Programme as a management tool under the ECC is a moving target, and as such it needs to be regularly updated and reviewed. This review period will depend upon the size/ scope of the project: on major projects, it could be done weekly, whereas on short-term, fast-track projects, (e.g. shop fit-outs), it may need to be daily.

There are tight timescales to be met on its submission and acceptance, and sending programme information backwards and forwards between the *Contractor's* and the *Client's* planners wastes valuable time.

To make it work to its full potential, an integrated programme is required and a planning team that monitors, reviews and agrees changes to the Accepted Programme on a continuous basis so that the submission of the programme as stated in the Contract Data becomes a mere formality.

The *Client* could also ensure that the Scope details the programme IT software requirements so that both sides are using the same software, facilitating quick and easy information transfer between them.

Because the programme is a moving target, the *Client's* planner needs to constantly check the dates by which, in order for the *Contractor* to Provide the Works, the *Client* is required to provide facilities, access, an updated Scope and so on. It should be noted that the *Client* has no obligation to provide 'things' earlier than the dates stated in the Scope.

If the *Contractor* should propose earlier dates than those shown for the *Client* to provide information or possession and so on, then the *Project Manager* should accept these earlier dates **if it is acceptable to the *Client***. If it is not, and the *Project Manager* accepts a programme showing earlier dates, then failure to meet these earlier dates will give rise to a compensation event.

2.13.5 What happens if the scope of the *works* is reduced or increased?

If you had a contract to build 2 km of new road and it was decided to reduce this to 1.9 km, then, all things being equal, planned Completion on the Accepted Programme would be earlier.

In Figure 2.5, line A shows the original *starting date*, *access date*, planned Completion and the Completion Date. In line B with the reduced scope, it can be seen that planned Completion moves forward, increasing the terminal float that is owned by the *Contractor*. The Completion Date does not move.

If later it is decided to increase the scope of the *works* back to the original scope then it can be seen in line C that planned Completion reverts to the date shown on the original programme, but because the *Contractor* owns the increased float, the Completion Date moves by the same amount as the planned Completion Date.

This is another subtle message to the *Client* to ensure that they know exactly what the scope of the work is.

2.13.6 What happens if the activities on the revised programme do not match the *activity schedule*?

The contract requires that the activities on the *activity schedule* **must relate to the programme** (Options A and C only). If they do not, then there exists the potential problem whereby delays could occur to an activity that is listed on the *activity schedule* but that does not appear in the programme. At this point the programme fails to be a useful management tool.

Figure 2.5 Reducing and increasing the scope of the *works*

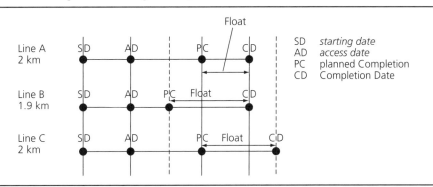

If this occurs, the *Project Manager* should not accept the revised programme, assuming that the start and finish date of each activity are shown. They should ask the *Contractor* under clauses 32.2 and 55.2 to submit a revision of the *activity schedule* to the *Project Manager* for acceptance.

The *Contractor* is at a disadvantage at this stage because if the *Project Manager* has not accepted a revised programme, they can make their own assessment of a compensation event.

2.13.7 What happens if the *Contractor* fails to maintain an Accepted Programme?

In this instance, the onus to maintain an up-to-date programme would seem to fall upon the *Project Manager*. It is not a strict contract requirement, but programme maintenance is necessary for the *Client's* right to levy delay damages, otherwise they will be frustrated. The *Project Manager* will need to have the capability to manage the programme so that they can make *Project Manager's* assessments for compensation events. In this instance, the *Project Manager* can reject all quotations submitted by a *Contractor* because they have not maintained an Accepted Programme.

2.13.8 The importance of good site records

Good site records (see Chapter 1 of Book Five for more information on site records) are an essential tool in the management of time, and it is essential that the *Supervisor* realises the importance of keeping good site diaries and how this information assists in the overall management of the contract.

For example, the site diary can be invaluable in establishing the events that took place on any particular day in the case of compensation events over causes of and responsibility for delay and/or disruption.

> Good site records can prove invaluable in establishing the facts and events when assessing compensation events.

Managing the Contract
ISBN 978-0-7277-6186-6

ICE Publishing: All rights reserved
http://dx.doi.org/10.1680/mc.61866.039

Chapter 3
Control of quality

Synopsis

This chapter discusses

- the quality framework embedded within the ECC
- the *Contractor's* obligations
- role of the *Client's* representatives
- subcontracting
- quality control.

3.1. Introduction

Construction contracts have traditionally had embedded within them a 'quality framework' providing the following features:

- rights of access for the client or their representative
- powers and duties given to the client or their representative relating to quality control
- powers for the client or their representative to deal with defective work
- powers of enforcement in case the *Contractor* does not respond.

This quality framework is the contractual approach to assuring quality. It is intended to establish quality requirements, ensure compliance and avoid defects as far as possible and to deal with defects without recourse to legal proceedings.

The latest extension of quality management principles in construction is a movement towards increasing reliance on inspection and testing by contractors, whether of their own work or of work produced by their subcontractors.

The rest of this chapter sets out to analyse how quality standards are set down in the ECC and to consider how comfortably this sits with the quality management principles and practices reflected in the current quality standards (BN EN ISO 9001, 9002 and 9003).

3.2. The ECC and quality

It is intended to analyse the particular clauses constituting the quality framework contained within the ECC under the following main headings:

- The *Contractor's* obligations
- The role of the *Client's* representatives with respect to quality
- The *Client's* supply
- Subcontracting
- Quality control
- Defective work
- Certification
- Enforcement.

Figure 3.1 shows these elements of control of quality on an ECC contract in diagrammatic form.

Figure 3.1 Control of quality in the ECC

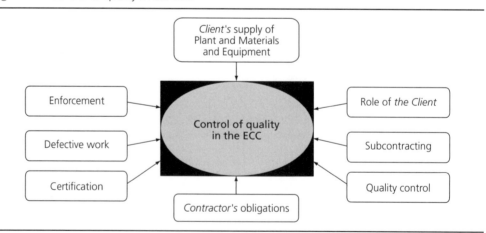

3.3. The *Contractor's* obligations
3.3.1 General obligations

The *Contractor's* general responsibility for quality is part of their wider duty to Provide the Works in accordance with the Scope (clause 20.1). Expanding this duty in line with the defined terms, the *Contractor* is responsible for doing 'the work necessary to complete the *works* in accordance with the contract and all incidental work, services and actions which the contract requires' (clause 11.2(15)).

The Scope is part of the contract, its purpose being to specify and describe the *works* and to describe any constraints on how the *Contractor* Provides the Works. It follows, therefore, that the quality standards to be achieved by the *Contractor* should be specified in the Scope prepared by or on behalf of the *Client*, and these standards are vitally important to quality control since they provide the basis upon which the existence of a Defect is judged (see Section 3.7.3 below on tests and inspections).

In addition, the Scope is required to describe the following aspects of quality control:

■ a quality management system
■ the quality policy statement and quality plan.

The *Contractor* is required to submit a quality policy statement and quality plan to the *Project Manager* for acceptance, and a revised quality policy statement and quality plan if it (the *Contractor*) makes any changes. The *Project Manager* will monitor compliance with the quality plan, and can instruct the *Contractor* to correct a failure in the quality plan.

> The *Contractor's* general responsibility is to Provide the Works in accordance with the Scope.
>
> The quality standards to be achieved by the *Contractor* should be specified in the Scope.

One of the objectives set by the NEC's drafting panel was that the contract should contribute to a reduction in the incidence of disputes. One of the improvements it sought to introduce in pursuit of this objective was clarity. It therefore follows, if the objectives of the contract are not to be undermined, that the quality standards described in the Scope should be expressed so that compliance is capable of objective assessment. This approach is entirely compatible with the principles of quality management, which demand that the supplier (*Contractor* or Subcontractor) should be able to verify compliance directly without reference to the purchaser (*Client* or their representative). Consequently, as far as it is practicable, the traditional specifying of requirements by reference to the opinion of the *Client* (or their *Supervisor*) should be eliminated from the Scope.

> The quality standards described in the Scope should be expressed so that compliance is capable of objective assessment.
>
> Specifying requirements by reference to the opinion of the *Project Manager* should be eliminated from the Scope.

3.3.2 Ambiguities and inconsistencies (discrepancies) in or between the contract documents

A difficult area concerns identification by the *Contractor* of discrepancies in the contract documentation. As a general principle, the economic achievement of quality is assisted by the identification of such shortcomings at the earliest possible stage of the construction process. The ECC is entirely consistent with this principle, placing upon both the *Contractor* and the *Project Manager* in clause 17.1 the obligation to give a notification as soon as one or other of them becomes aware of an ambiguity or inconsistency in or between the documents comprising the contract. The *Project Manager* then has the responsibility for instructing the resolution of the ambiguity or inconsistency.

> There is an obligation on the *Contractor* and *Project Manager* to give a notification as soon as they become aware of an ambiguity or inconsistency.
>
> The *Project Manager* resolves any ambiguities and inconsistencies between contractual documents by giving an instruction.

Provisions in some standard forms of contract for reimbursement to the contractor because of such discrepancies in contract documentation act as a disincentive to the contractor to comment before the contract is let, and a possible disincentive to early reporting after the contract is let.

Likewise, when using some standard forms of contract, which envisage the same organisation preparing the contract documentation and administering it, there may be reluctance on the part of individuals to draw attention to discrepancies in documentation which their company prepared.

The ECC encourages both Parties to notify as soon as they become aware of anything that may affect the cost, time or quality of the *works*. The *Contractor* is incentivised to notify as soon as they become aware of these matters. The sanction for failure to do so is that they run the risk of losing their full entitlement to the time and cost consequences of the event.

The *Client's* sanction is that they could spend more time and more money and not get the quality they were hoping for. For the *Project Manager* and *Supervisor*, there is no hiding place and their actions/inactions will be highly visible.

A concept **not** found in the ECC is a hierarchy of the documents forming the contract. Such a hierarchy is used in some standard forms as a means of resolving ambiguities and discrepancies by giving precedence to documents higher up the contractual hierarchy. With one exception to this general rule (see below), the ECC contains no such hierarchy. Instead, very simply, having been notified of an ambiguity or inconsistency, the *Project Manager* resolves the problem by instructing a change to the Scope. This of course is a compensation event, and by the operation of clause 63.8 any assessment is based on the interpretation most favourable to the Party **not** responsible for the ambiguity/inconsistency; that is, the *contra proferentem* rule operates, which interprets a clause containing an ambiguity or inconsistency against the Party responsible for drafting the document in which it occurs.

In the ECC the concept of 'Key Dates' is added to 'the Prices' and 'the Completion Date' as a matter for early warning.

The one exception to the 'no-hierarchy' concept is where an inconsistency becomes apparent between the Scope provided by the *Client* and a design that is part of the Scope provided by the *Contractor* and referenced in Contract Data part two. On the assumption, in this instance, that having been notified of the ambiguity/inconsistency, the *Project Manager's* instruction required the design to comply with the *Client's* Scope, such a change would **not** be a compensation event (see the second bullet point of clause 60.1(1)). This effectively gives precedence to the Scope provided by the *Client* over the Scope provided by the *Contractor*.

There is no hierarchy of documents in the ECC.

The *contra proferentem* rule applies to the Scope.

3.3.3 The *Contractor's* design

There is no '*Contractor* design' version of the ECC. That is not to say the contract does not provide specifically for all or part of the *works* to be designed by the *Contractor*: on the contrary, it offers the flexibility of being suitable for both 'traditional' arrangements where the permanent *works* are designed by or on behalf of the *Client* and for 'design-and-build' arrangements where the *Contractor* designs and builds the whole of the *works* in accordance with criteria set down by the *Client*. Between these two extremes it is suitable for the many instances where the *Contractor* does some design and some is done by, or on behalf of, the *Client*.

But how is this flexibility achieved? Very simply, the ECC requires the Scope to state the parts of the *works* that the *Contractor* is to design and the criteria to which such designs are required to conform. Such criteria could include details of the form, geometry, dimensions, specifications, codes of practice, standards and environmental criteria, or alternatively could comprise a performance specification where the *Contractor* is responsible for the majority of the design. If, after having let the contract, it is decided to increase or decrease the areas of the *works* that the *Contractor* is to design, or to change the criteria to which they are already designing, such changes would be in the form of instructions changing the Scope and would consequently be a compensation event.

> The Scope should state the parts of the *works* that the *Contractor* is to design.

3.3.4 Supervision/ employees

Contrary to many quality assurance practitioners' belief, quality is not achieved by procedures, it is achieved by people. Procedures do not take decisions, people do.

You could have the best procedures in the world and still not achieve quality – there has to be a combination of both people and procedures to achieve the desired quality.

Neither the traditional standard forms of contract nor the published quality standards have placed enough emphasis on the competence (quality) of people. Competency is a function of knowledge and skills gained from education, training and/or experience.

The ECC (clause 24.1) places an obligation on the *Contractor* to employ the key persons named by the *Contractor* in Contract Data part two to do the jobs designated to them therein. If maximum value is to be gained from this feature of the ECC, the *Client* should indicate in the instructions to tenderers the key persons for whom details (including job description, responsibilities, qualifications and experience) are required. Such information when received with tenders should then be assessed as part of the wider tender evaluation (see Appendix 1 of Book Two).

Clause 24.1 also requires that if the *Contractor* wishes to provide replacement people, they must provide people of equal quality and ability. This feature has been introduced so that the *Contractor* provides the required quality of people, such as the 'A' team as outlined in their tender submission. Very often in the past, contracts were awarded on the basis of the curricula vitae put forward, only for the *Client* to find that these people did not put in an appearance on the contract.

> People achieve quality.
>
> The *Client* should indicate in the instructions to tenderers the key persons for whom details are required.

The ECC in clause 24.2 also recognises that the *Project Manager* should be able to have an employee removed from the project.

3.3.5 The mode and method of construction

It is often overlooked that any reference in the ECC to the programme includes method statements. Clause 31.2 requires the *Contractor* to include for each operation a statement of how the *Contractor* plans to do the work, identifying the principal Equipment and resources they plan to use. This book refers to these statements as method statements and resource statements.

Any reference in the ECC to the programme includes the *Contractor* providing a statement of how they plan to do the work.

The traditional reason for asking for method statements, particularly in civil engineering contracts, is to allow the designer of the permanent works (traditionally the engineer) to check that the proposed methods of construction will not have a detrimental effect on any partly completed permanent *works*. It is often overlooked by the drafters of ECC-related contract documentation that, unless the Scope specifically precludes particular methods of construction, any constraints subsequently introduced would under the ECC constitute a change to the Scope and would consequently be a compensation event. This is particularly relevant on *works* involving heavy foundation engineering where the trend is to reduce the need for (and accordingly the cost of) temporary earthwork support systems by exploiting the ability of the permanent structure to provide such support during construction. This applies notably to the technique of 'top-down' construction and the use of embedded peripheral walls (e.g. secant/contiguous piled walls and diaphragm walls).

The Management of Health and Safety at Work Regulations 1999 (and subsequent amendments) provides that if *Contractor* is to carry out work that has risks to health and safety (and most construction activities do), they have a legal duty to carry out a risk assessment. Although not required by law, preparing a written method statement after carrying out a risk assessment has proved to be an effective way of producing an action plan identifying the necessary health and safety measures to be employed to control the risks identified. If it is likely that the *Project Manager* will want to see safety method statements (as evidence that the required risk assessments have been undertaken), then it is probably wise to include a statement to this effect in the Scope describing the health and safety requirements (clause 27.4).

It is worth re-emphasising that the ECC treats method statements submitted by the *Contractor* as part of the programme, and consequently the reasons for not accepting the programme apply equally to these method statements, the reasons being that the method statements

- are not practicable
- do not show the information that the contract requires (e.g. they do not identify the Equipment and other resources that the *Contractor* plans to use)
- do not represent the *Contractor's* plans realistically
- do not comply with the Scope; for example, they may show that the *Contractor* plans to employ a method of construction that is expressly precluded by the Scope.

Acceptance of a programme (and therefore method statements), unlike acceptance of the *Contractor's* design, is not a condition precedent to the *Contractor* proceeding with the work. Failure by the *Contractor* to submit at the required times, or a decision by the *Project Manager* not to accept a revised programme (and therefore revised method statements), does not require the *Contractor* to stop work. A lack of attention, however, by the *Contractor* to their obligations regarding programmes and method statements does under the ECC expose the *Contractor* to the risk of the *Project Manager* carrying out their own assessments of any compensation events that arise (refer to clause 64.1, third and fourth bullet points).

3.3.6 Setting out

Unlike most other standard forms of contract, the ECC does not contain an express condition making the *Contractor* responsible for the setting out of the *works*. It is arguable that the definition of 'to Provide the Works' (clause 11.2(15)) is sufficiently wide to include setting out, since it includes all incidental works and services. Since the *Contractor* is required to Provide the Works 'in accordance with the Scope' (in clause 20.1, describing the *Contractor's* primary obligation), it is recommended that the Scope makes it clear that the setting out of the *works* is the *Contractor's* responsibility.

> The Scope needs to include a statement with regard to the *Contractor's* responsibility for setting out the *works*.

3.3.7 Quality management systems

Clauses 40.1, 40.2 and 40.3 of the ECC require the *Contractor*

- to operate a quality management system complying with the requirements stated in the Scope
- to submit to the *Project Manager* for acceptance (within the period in the Contract Data) a quality policy statement and a quality plan that must allow the *Contractor* to Provide the Works
- to comply with any instruction from the *Project Manager* to correct a non-compliance with the quality plan, and this instruction will not be a compensation event.

Bearing in mind these requirements, the following observations are made:

- Unless the Scope describes both the requirements for the quality management system and states the information that the quality policy statement and quality plans are to include so that the *Contractor* knows what is needed to Provide the Works, the clauses will be of limited effect.

- The *Contractor* can change the quality plan, but it must then submit the changed quality plan to the *Project Manager* for acceptance.
- As with all other instances where the *Project Manager's* acceptance is required, if they withhold acceptance for a reason other than one stated in the contract, a compensation event arises (clause 60.1(9)).
- Acceptance by the *Project Manager* of the *Contractor's* quality policy statement and quality plan is not intended to change the *Contractor's* liabilities or their responsibilities to Provide the Works (clause 14.1). This is very important with respect to quality plans: there is no guarantee that the end-product requirements for the *works* (as described in the Scope) would be met just because the *Contractor* faithfully adheres to the documented procedures and instructions.
- The period stated (calculated from the *starting date*) for submission by the *Contractor* of the quality policy statement and quality plan should be mindful of the need to have these documents in place before any serious work is commenced. To speed up the process, it may be worth considering asking *Contractor*s to include with their tender submissions an overall outline quality plan and a detailed quality plan covering the first 6 weeks' activities (see Appendix 1 of Book Two).
- The Scope should set out the degree of involvement of the *Project Manager* in terms of their 'external supervision' of the *Contractor's* quality management system (external audits, hold and witness points expressly required, etc.).
- Non-compliance with the quality management system, such as a failure to keep records, does not necessarily cause any material loss or damage or give rise to a Defect, but confidence in the system demands full compliance. Consequently, the wording of clause 40.3 that allows the *Project Manager* to instruct the *Contractor* 'to correct a failure to comply with the quality plan' facilitates correction of a non-compliance with the quality plan even though there may be no evidence of a Defect as defined by the contract (clause 11.2(6)). Of course, if the *Project Manager* considers that the nature of the non-compliance is highly likely to have given rise to a Defect, they can ask the *Supervisor* to instruct a search (refer to clause 43.1, and Section 3.4.2 below).

3.4. The role of the *Client's* representatives with respect to quality

The ECC envisages two '*Client's* representatives': the *Project Manager* and the *Supervisor*.

The *Project Manager's* role is to manage the contract on behalf of the *Client* with the intention of achieving the *Client's* objectives (usually expressed in terms of a budget, a programme and a brief setting out the requirements for the end-product). The *Project Manager's* authority under the contract is expressed in terms of the actions that the contract prescribes to them, and includes authority to change the Scope, to instruct the *Contractor* to do various things, including to correct a failure to comply with the quality plan, and to generally exercise their managerial and engineering judgement.

The *Supervisor* has a much more restricted role, effectively limited to ensuring that the *works* are constructed in accordance with the Scope. The importance of the role should not be underestimated, given its obvious connection with one of the *Client's* objectives: namely to ensure that the end-product meets the requirements set out in the *Client's* brief. The ECC Guidance Notes do not explain why the drafters of the contract considered it necessary to split duties between the *Project Manager* and the *Supervisor*, although it is likely that they considered there to be a potential conflict between getting the *works* constructed to budget and time while at the same time achieving the required quality.

The practical effect of splitting the role, however, would appear to require the *Client* to resolve any such conflicts given the direct reporting lines that both the *Project Manager* and *Supervisor* enjoy, and the ECC Guidance Notes do concede 'that the roles of the *Project Manager* and the *Supervisor* may be combined where the objectives of the *Client* are served by so doing'.

It is not intended to go into great depth in this part of the chapter as to the role of the representatives in the context of 'control of quality' other than to list the actions (see Appendix 2 of Book One) which they are required to take, more of which is discussed in the relevant parts of this chapter. See also the publication *NEC4: The Role of the Supervisor*, by Mitchell and Trebes (ICE, 2018).

3.4.1 The *Project Manager*

The *Project Manager's* actions with respect to quality include

- giving instructions changing the Scope
- giving instructions resolving ambiguities or inconsistencies between the documents that are part of the contract
- acceptance of the *Contractor's* design for any parts of the *works* and for items of Equipment
- acceptance of replacement key persons
- acceptance of Subcontractors, the proposed subcontract documents (in certain circumstances) and the proposed pricing information (in certain circumstances)
- acceptance of method statements and the rest of the programme
- giving instructions to stop or not to start any work
- deciding the date of and certifying Completion
- acceptance of the *Contractor's* quality policy statement and quality plan
- giving instructions to the *Contractor* to correct a failure to comply with the quality plan
- assessing amounts payable by the *Contractor* to the *Client* in respect of costs incurred by the *Client* and Others resulting from a test or inspection having to be repeated after a Defect is found
- arranging for the *Client* to give access to the *Contractor* to parts of the *works* already taken over by the *Client* if needed to correct Defects
- proposing changes to the Scope so that Defects do not have to be corrected
- arranging to have Defects corrected by people other than the *Contractor* where the latter has not corrected them within the *defect correction period*
- requesting proof of the *Contractor's* title to documents, Equipment, Plant and Materials prior to inclusion of the value of same in assessments of the amount due
- giving instructions on how to deal with objects of value or of historical or other interest found within the site.

3.4.2 The *Supervisor*

The *Supervisor's* actions with respect to quality include

- notifying the *Contractor* of any tests and inspections that the *Supervisor* wishes to carry out
- watching any tests done by the *Contractor*
- notifying the results of tests and inspections
- notifying the *Contractor* that Plant and Materials outside the Working Areas have passed any tests or inspections that the Scope makes a precondition for their being brought to the Working Areas
- giving instructions to search that may include
  - uncovering, dismantling, recovering and re-erecting work
  - doing tests and inspections that the Scope does not require
- notifying the *Contractor* of any Defects found
- issuing the Defects Certificate
- marking documents, Equipment, Plant and Materials outside the Working Areas in order to secure for the *Client* whatever title the *Contractor* has.

3.4.3 The *Client*

The *Client's* actions with respect to quality include

- providing facilities, materials and samples for tests and inspections done by the *Supervisor* as stated in the Scope
- giving access to the *Contractor* to parts of the *works* already taken over by the *Client* if needed to correct Defects.

3.5. The *Client's* supply
3.5.1 Plant and Materials, facilities and services

It is not unusual for *Clients* to provide things to the *Contractor*, either for inclusion in the *works* or to be used for (but not included in) the *works*. The terms used for these two categories of things by the ECC is 'Plant and Materials' and 'facilities and services', one definition of the latter being 'items provided by the *Client* for use by the *Contractor* to Provide the Works but which the Scope does not require the *Contractor* to include in the *works*', such as common-user construction plant and welfare facilities. Note that Equipment is provided by the *Contractor* by definition (clause 11.2(9)), and therefore items of plant provided by the **Client** for use by the

Contractor to Provide the Works but that the Scope does not require the *Contractor* to include in the *works* cannot also be called Equipment.

The provision of Plant and Materials or facilities and services by the *Client* brings with it attendant risks, which, like all risks, are best avoided unless the benefits justify such a course of action. The ECC recognises that there may be times when the *Client* wishes to provide things to the *Contractor* but makes it clear where the risk lies in the event that things do not go according to plan. The two risks the *Client* carries are

- that the *Client* does not provide something they are to provide by the date shown in the Accepted Programme (Compensation event in clause 60.1(3))
- a *Client's* liability event occurs (compensation event 60.1(14)), which in this context could be 'loss of or damage to [things] supplied to the *Contractor* by the *Client*, or by Others on the *Client's* behalf, until the *Contractor* has received and accepted them' (clause 80.1).

The ECC sensibly leaves it to the Scope to describe the 'things' to be provided by the *Client* and a 'no earlier than' time for delivery. The *Project Manager* would then, as part of the tender assessment, need to check that the dates for requiring such things shown in the programme submitted by the tenderers with their tenders complied with the Scope before affording them Accepted Programme status.

To protect themselves from the second of the risks identified above, the *Client* would be well advised to ensure that the Scope includes, for things to be provided, clear procedures that leave the Parties in no doubt as to the point in time when the *Contractor* is deemed to have received and accepted the things (effectively the risk-transfer point in terms of responsibility for care).

3.5.2 Other contractors

The ECC defines 'Others' as 'people or organisations who are not the *Client*, the *Project Manager*, the *Supervisor*, the *Adjudicator* or a member of the Dispute Avoidance Board, the *Contractor* or any employee, Subcontractor or supplier of the *Contractor*' (clause 11.2(12)). Consequently, other contractors interfacing with the *Contractor* would be a sub-category of Others as defined.

Clause 25.1 of the ECC describes the extent of the *Contractor's* obligations with regard to the interface with Others, namely

- to co-operate with Others in obtaining and providing information that they need in connection with the *works*
- share the Working Areas with Others as stated in the Scope.

Interface management is discussed further in Chapter 4 of Book Two.

To summarise, the *Contractor* is not responsible for the failure of other Parties to carry out their work in accordance with the Scope unless the *Contractor's* non-co-operation causes the failure.

> The Scope should include interface schedules for the work of Others.

3.6. Subcontracting

A Subcontractor is defined by the ECC (clause 11.2(19)) as follows:

'A Subcontractor is a person or organisation who has a contract with the *Contractor* to

- construct or install part of the *works*,
- design all or part of the *works*, except the design of Plant and Materials carried out by the supplier or
- provide a service in the Working Areas which is necessary to Provide the Works, except for the
  - hire of Equipment or
  - supply of people paid for by the *Contractor* according to the time they work.'

Given the tendency today for main contractors to subcontract a large part of the work, it is clearly important for the purposes of quality that care is exercised over the selection of Sub-contractors; particularly since quality management systems and quality assurance may not be given sufficient emphasis in these organisations. It is not only the *Client* who needs to be aware of the subcontracting arrangements. A *Contractor* will be fully liable to the *Client* for the faults of a Subcontractor (clause 26.1), and although they may in turn have a right to recover from the Subcontractor, if that Subcontractor has gone into liquidation or has insufficient assets, the *Contractor* will be left to bear the liability, however expertly drafted the terms of the subcontract.

It is therefore very much in a *Contractor's* interest to minimise the likelihood of defects occurring and to be able to demonstrate clearly that they have fulfilled their contractual obligations. With these objectives in mind, the *Contractor* should not only implement a quality system covering their own activities but also ensure either that their Subcontractors in turn implement their own quality system (preferable) or that their own quality system is sufficient to verify the Subcontractor's work. Clause 26.1 of the ECC states, 'if the *Contractor* subcontracts work, it is responsible for Providing the Works as if it had not subcontracted'. This makes it clear that the *Contractor's* quality management system, quality policy statement and quantity plan **must** cover any work that the *Contractor* chooses to subcontract.

In general terms, the ECC provides for the *Contractor* to subcontract all, some or none of the works, provided that the *Project Manager* accepts the proposed Subcontractors. The appointment of a Subcontractor for substantial work before acceptance by the *Project Manager* is expressly made grounds for termination of the contract (clause 91.2 (R13)).

Traditionally, one way that employers and their representatives have exercised a degree of control through contracts over the 'quality' of Subcontractors, particularly for specialist work, is by the process of nomination. The ECC however does **not** provide for the nomination of Sub-contractors due, the ECC Guidance Notes explain, to 'the legal and practical problems of accountability which frequently ensue', which in turn conflict with the principle (as embodied in clause 26.1) that the *Contractor* should be fully responsible for every aspect of the work that they have contracted for. Alternatives under the ECC to nominating Subcontractors suggested by the ECC Guidance Notes include

- leaving the *Contractor* freedom to subcontract as they think fit, with the *Project Manager* retaining some control over the identity of any proposed Subcontractors (see below)
- providing lists of acceptable Subcontractors in the Scope for particular parts of the *works*
- providing for separate contracts with the *Client*, with the *Project Manager* managing the time and physical interfaces between them (not subcontracting within the accepted meaning of the term).

If a *Contractor*, under the ECC, decides to subcontract a part of the *works*, it is not permitted to appoint the proposed Subcontractor until the *Project Manager* has accepted both the Subcontractor (in all cases) and the proposed subcontract documents (unless the proposed sub-contract is an NEC contract that has not been amended other than in accordance with the *additional conditions of contract* or the *Project Manager* has decided that it does not require to see the proposed conditions). A reason for not accepting either the proposed Subcontractor or the proposed conditions of contract is that they will not allow the *Contractor* to Provide the Works.

It is open to some debate as to both why a *Contractor* would want to engage a Subcontractor who would not allow them to Provide the Works and on what basis the *Project Manager* could decide that a proposed Subcontractor would not allow the *Contractor* to Provide the Works. It is suggested that one way to reduce possible disputes on the issue is to include in the Scope minimum requirements in respect of procurement procedures to be followed by the *Contractor* (to be developed by the *Contractor* as part of their quality plan) and minimum qualifying criteria for Subcontractors. An example is given below.

> The Subcontractor must have in place its own quality management system or ensure all employees are registered under construction skills certification schemes, or be able to demonstrate a minimum of 5 years' experience in their chosen field on subcontracts of an equivalent magnitude.

> Include in the Scope minimum requirements in respect of procurement procedures to be followed by the *Contractor*; for example, ensure value for money through term contracts or competitively tendering a minimum of three subcontractors.

3.7. Quality control
3.7.1 General

Having defined, by way of the drawings and specification, the work to be undertaken and the standards of material and workmanship required, construction contracts have traditionally included provisions setting out

- rights of access for the *Client* and their representatives
- powers and duties related to quality control
- powers to deal with defective work
- powers of enforcement and/or remedies in case the *Contractor* does not comply with their obligation to correct defective work.

The ECC includes such provisions that will be discussed under the headings of

- access for the *Client* and their representatives
- tests and inspections
- investigating defects and additional testing
- quality procedures.

The provisions setting out the *Client's* powers to deal with defective work and of enforcement are dealt with in Sections 3.8 and 3.10, respectively, of this chapter.

3.7.2 Access for the *Client* and their representative

The ECC (clause 27.2) provides very wide powers of access for the *Project Manager*, the *Supervisor* and Others as instructed by the *Project Manager*, to work being done and Plant and Materials being stored for the contract, wherever the work is being done. Such access is important for the purpose of checking on progress and for witnessing or carrying out tests and inspections.

3.7.3 Tests and inspections

The arrangements for inspection and testing should be clearly agreed between the Parties as part of the contract. The ECC seeks to achieve this by relying on the Scope to state the following:

- the nature of the tests/inspections to be done
- the timing of specified tests/inspections
- where the tests/inspections are to be done (e.g. within the Working Areas or before delivery to the Working Areas)
- who is responsible for doing the tests/inspections (e.g. the *Contractor*, the *Supervisor* or an outside testing agency)
- who is responsible for providing materials, facilities and samples for tests/inspections
- the objectives of the tests/inspections, the testing procedures to be applied and the standards to be satisfied.

Technical specifications (i.e. the Scope) should be prepared with a view to their function within a quality management system. They should therefore be practicable, realistic and capable of objective assessment by the *Contractor* without reference to the *Client's* representative (the *Supervisor*). This calls for great care in the drafting of the Scope and the elimination of phrases such as 'to the satisfaction of' and 'in the opinion of' the *Client's* representative.

There is a very strong case to be made for the standardisation of the *Client's* technical specifications

- to ensure that the information the ECC requires to be included in the Scope is actually present
- to facilitate the development of quality system procedures and processes by contractors (as required by clause 40 of the ECC).

> Clause 41 deals only with tests and inspections that are required by the Scope or the applicable law.

It is important to realise that clause 41 in the ECC that deals with tests and inspections only applies to tests and inspections required by the Scope or the applicable law (i.e. specified or statutory tests). It does not therefore apply to tests and inspections that the *Contractor* does at its own discretion or for its own purposes. This latter category of test/inspection could be quite extensive on contracts where the *Contractor* has a well-developed quality system in place where it is quite likely that the testing and inspection plan contained within the quality plan would require more extensive verification than that required by the Scope and the law.

The *Project Manager*, of course, does have the power to request additional tests and inspections to those required in the Scope by issuing an instruction changing the Scope (clause 14.3), but such an instruction would be treated as a compensation event (clause 60.1(1)).

In circumstances where the *Supervisor* is responsible for doing tests and inspections, clause 41.5 deals with the possibility that such tests or inspections cause unnecessary delay either to the work in hand or to any payment that is conditional upon a test or inspection being successful. Such an event becomes a compensation event if it can be established that the delay was 'unnecessary'.

Clause 41.3 of the ECC requires the *Contractor* and the *Project Manager* to notify each other before commencing tests and inspections and to notify each other of the results afterwards. This is in keeping with the contract's philosophy of ensuring that both Parties are kept informed of events and can respond quickly if, for example, tests reveal that any work does not comply with the standards specified in the Scope.

Clause 42.1 of the ECC deals with tests and inspections that the Scope expressly states are to be carried out on off-site Plant and Materials before the latter are delivered to the Working Areas. While this is a sensible provision designed to avoid the expense of transporting defective Plant and Materials back to the place of manufacture, the clause places the onus on the *Supervisor* to notify the *Contractor* that the particular Plant and Materials have passed the requisite tests and inspections. In instances where these tests and inspections are the responsibility of the *Contractor*, this will require the latter to first notify the *Supervisor* of the results of the off-site tests and inspections but then to wait for the *Supervisor's* acknowledgement (by way of notification) that the off-site Plant and Materials have indeed passed the prescribed tests and inspections.

3.7.4 Notifying and investigating Defects and additional testing

It is very important under the ECC to understand what the contract means when it uses the term 'Defect'. Clause 11.2(6) defines a Defect as

- a part of the *works* which is not in accordance with the Scope or
- a part of the *works* designed by the *Contractor* which is not in accordance with the applicable law or the *Contractor's* design which the *Project Manager* has accepted.

> A Defect can only be determined with reference to the Scope or the law.

There are a number of issues to appreciate from this definition:

- The quality standards stated in the Scope (prepared by the *Client*) provide the basis on which the existence of a Defect is judged. The importance of careful drafting of the technical standards is emphasised above.
- The definition **excludes** defects due to design for which the *Client* is responsible. Such defects would have to be dealt with by way of instructions from the *Project Manager*, and would invariably trigger the compensation event procedure.
- In instances where the *Contractor* is responsible for designing a part of the *works* and the *Project Manager* inadvertently accepts a design from the *Contractor* that does not comply with the Scope in some respect, contractually a Defect will still arise if the *works* are constructed to the latter design. This is the effect of the 'two-limb' definition of a Defect and why it is vitally important that the *Contractor* ensures that the Scope they prepare and submit for acceptance complies with the Scope prepared by the *Client*.
- A Defect as defined may include a departure by the *Contractor* from procedures or instructions set down in the *Contractor's* quality management system (including the quality plan) for the *works*, where the *Contractor's* quality system is included in the Scope provided by the *Contractor*.

Having established what the contract means by the term 'Defect', how does it deal with the notification and investigation of Defects? Clause 43.2 states that 'until the *defects date* the *Supervisor* and the *Contractor* notify the other as soon as they become aware of a Defect'. Simplicity itself, although, somewhat unusually for construction contracts, this places a contractual obligation on the *Contractor* to admit openly that they have got something wrong. Although unusual for construction contracts, this is entirely consistent with both the quality standards and the ECC philosophy of enabling problems to be identified as soon as possible in order that they can be dealt with properly.

Both the *Supervisor* and the *Contractor* are obliged to notify each other of Defects.

If no Defect has been notified by the *Contractor* but the *Supervisor* suspects one may exist, clause 43.1 gives the *Supervisor* the power to instruct the *Contractor* to 'search' for a Defect, which may include

- uncovering, dismantling, recovering and re-erecting work
- providing facilities, materials and samples for tests and inspections done by the *Supervisor* (which by implication are additional to any stated in the Scope)
- doing tests and inspections that the Scope does not require.

If a search is instructed and a Defect is discovered (i.e. non-compliance with the Scope), the *Contractor* corrects the Defect, and no compensation event arises. Conversely, if no Defect is discovered, the *Contractor* is entitled to a compensation event unless the search was needed only because the *Contractor* gave insufficient notice of doing work obstructing a required test or inspection (clause 60.1(10)).

3.7.5 Quality procedures   Experience has shown that reliance on contracts alone as a means of assuring quality in construction has not met with the expectations of many clients of the industry. Consequently, forward-thinking clients have taken the lead in promoting the adoption, development and implementation of quality management systems by their suppliers (contractors/consultants). The quality management system and contractual approach to assuring quality are neither mutually exclusive of one another nor mutually dependent; they are concurrent means of assuring quality. However, an integrated approach is necessary to maximise the advantage and avoid the potential disadvantages from adopting both. This demands careful drafting of contracts and their supporting documentation (e.g. Scope) by professionals who understand both the fundamentals of quality systems and contracts and the interaction between the two.

In order to make the most of clause 40, a *Client* will need several things:

- details of what they expect of the *Contractor's* quality management system so that these requirements can be included in the Scope
- a *Project Manager* (or perhaps an internal/external quality consultant to whom the work in this clause has been delegated) who
  - knows what to expect of the *Contractor's* quality policy statement and a quality plan that is submitted to them for acceptance
  - who can determine whether the submitted documents will 'allow' the *Contractor* to Provide the Works
  - knows the *Contractor's* quality plan well enough that they can recognise a failure to comply with the quality plan and determine whether the failure is important enough that they would instruct a correction of a failure to comply with the quality plan.

Although these requirements are the *Project Manager's* duties, the *Client* may consider them to be more in line with the *Supervisor's* duties, and the *Client* may choose to include them in the *Supervisor's* personal contract along with liaison requirements with the *Project Manager*.

3.8. Defective work
3.8.1 General

Defective work will be discussed under the following headings:

- rejection
- correction of Defects
- the defects liability period
- concessions.

3.8.2 Rejection of the *works*

The ECC does not contain any express provision for rejection of a part of, or the whole of, the *works* in the event that the performance of the same is wholly unacceptable when judged against the requirements of the Scope. Such an occurrence could arise when a *Contractor* responsible for designing and constructing the *works* fails to meet a performance specification expressed in terms of the efficiency of the completed *works* (not uncommon in the process and plant sector).

Instead, the ECC provides for various possible remedies, in that Defects are addressed depending on the seriousness of the failure. These include

- the *Contractor* is required to correct Defects (see Section 3.8.3 below)
- the Defect is accepted and the contract price is reduced (see Section 3.8.5)
- the *Contractor* is liable for the cost of having Defects corrected by Others (see Section 3.10.4)
- low-performance damages secondary Option X17 (see Section 3.10.5).

3.8.3 Correction of Defects

The *Contractor* has an obligation (clause 44.1) to 'correct a Defect whether or not the *Supervisor* notifies it'. This might seem like stating the obvious but it does emphasise the importance of the quality standards specified in the Scope being capable of objective assessment, removing reliance on the *Client's* representatives as the arbiter of what is acceptable and what is not.

> The *Contractor* is required to correct Defects whether or not the *Supervisor* has notified the *Contractor* of them.

In terms of when the *Contractor* has to correct Defects, the ECC takes a practical approach, and **up to Completion** (of either a *section* or the whole of the *works*) generally leaves the timing of corrective works to suit the *Contractor's* planning. There are, however, incentives for the *Contractor* to correct Defects sooner rather than later. These are as follows:

- For the price-based main Options of the ECC, only completed activities/work that is 'without notified Defects the correction of which will delay following work' is taken into consideration when assessing interim payments to the *Contractor* (clauses A11.2(29) and B11.2(30)).

- For cost-based options, Defects corrected after Completion are a Disallowed Cost.
- The *Project Manager* has no duty to certify Completion (of any *section* or the whole of the *works*) until the *Contractor* has corrected Defects which would prevent the *Client* from using the *works* (or Others from doing their work (clause 11.2(2)). This has the double downside of both preventing the release of half of any retention held (where secondary Option X16 is used) and increasing the likelihood of the *Contractor's* exposure to delay damages (where secondary Option X7 is used).
- The *Contractor* is required to show on each revised programme that they submit to the *Project Manager* for acceptance how they plan to correct notified Defects.
- If there are many notified Defects, the *Contractor* might struggle to correct all of them within the *defect correction period* after Completion. It could be more efficient for the *Contractor* to correct the Defects at the time of notification while the resources are on Site and working in that area.

If a test or inspection shows that any work has a Defect, clause 41.4 states that the *Contractor* corrects the Defect and then repeats the test or inspection that led to its discovery.

Completion of the *works* (or any *section* of it) is a significant milestone in determining the time within which the *Contractor* has to correct any Defects that still exist at that time or that subsequently come to light. This is because clause 44.2 places on the *Contractor* an obligation to correct notified Defects before the end of the '*defect correction period*'. The *defect correction period* begins at Completion for Defects notified before Completion (other than those that would prevent the *Client* from using the *works*, which by this time should no longer exist) and when the Defect is notified for other Defects – that is, those notified after Completion. The *defect correction period* being an italicised term in the ECC means that it must be given meaning by an entry in the Contract Data. Typically, *Clients* prescribe a period of 2 or 3 weeks.

Invariably there will be instances when Defects are discovered after Completion when the *Client* has taken over the *works*. Clause 44.4 of the ECC deals with such a situation by requiring the *Project Manager* to arrange for the *Client* to give 'access to and use of a part of the *works* which has been taken over if it is needed for correcting a Defect'.

Defects notified before Completion must be corrected within the *defect correction period* after Completion.

Defects notified before Completion that would prevent the *Client* from using the *works* must be corrected before Completion.

Defects notified after Completion must be corrected within the *defect correction period* after notification.

For maintenance contracts that use the ECC rather than the NEC4 Term Service Contract, it is important that Defects are corrected at the time of notification and not left until after Completion to be corrected. If it is important that Defects are corrected at the time of notification, clause 44.2 can be amended using Option Z (the second sentence in clause 44.2 is deleted and replaced as follows: 'This period begins when the Defect is notified').

3.8.4 The Defects liability period

It should by now be realised that the term *defect correction period* as used by the ECC has a wholly different meaning from other similar phrases such as 'defects liability period' and 'maintenance periods' used in other standard forms. The *defect correction period* in the ECC is simply the time that the *Contractor* has to correct notified Defects existing at or arising after Completion.

So how does the ECC define the period within which the *Contractor* is contractually liable to correct Defects arising in the *works*? It uses the expression '*defects date*' that, given its italicised status, requires it to be given effect by the *Client* inserting a period of weeks (typically 52 weeks) in Contract Data part one, a period that runs from the date of Completion decided by the *Project Manager*.

There is no obligation on the *Contractor* to notify Completion.

3.8.5 Concessions

Most traditional standard forms of contract do not cater adequately for rational decisions about defective work based on engineering considerations. Consider an example where contiguous piles forming the embedded walls to a shaft have been sunk outside the vertical tolerances required by the Scope. Most engineers will appreciate that the cost, time and effort necessary to remedy this situation may be out of all proportion to the impact that the Defect has on following work and, indeed, the completed *works*. Previously the *Client's* representative, faced with such a situation, had the following options:

- Turn a blind eye.
- Accept the Defect (although not permitted by the contract) with the consequent attendant implications if the result is unsatisfactory.
- Play it 'by the book', demanding 'unreasonable' steps to correct the Defect out of all proportion to the likely impact of the Defect on the finished works. Such a course of action has the undesirable side-effect of encouraging the *Contractor* not to notify similar Defects in the future.

The ECC fortunately sweeps all this away by incorporating a very practical provision, setting in train the possibility of acceptance of a Defect if the *Contractor* and the *Project Manager* so agree. Clause 45.1 simply permits either to propose to the other that the Scope should be changed so that the Defect does not have to be corrected. The subtlety of this is that by changing the Scope in such an instance, the Defect ceases to exist and consequently any later adverse implications of such 'acceptance' of the Defect are at the *Client's* risk. Obviously, great care is required on the part of the *Project Manager*, who would invariably seek advice from their designers and/or engineers in such a situation. The machinery for such a concession is set out in clause 45.2 and involves the following steps:

1. The *Project Manager* and the *Contractor* decide whether they are prepared to consider a change to the Scope so that a Defect does not have to be corrected (in practice, the proposal is likely to be initiated by the *Contractor*).
2. If they are, the *Contractor* submits a quotation for **reduced** Prices (a saving to the *Client*) or an earlier Completion Date or both to the *Project Manager* for acceptance (effectively the *Contractor's* 'consideration' in return for the *Client's* loss of value).
3. The *Project Manager* either
   - accepts the quotation and instructs the necessary change to the Scope, the Prices, Key Dates and the Completion Date accordingly and accepts the revised programme or
   - does not accept the quotation, leaving the *Contractor* either to correct the Defect or submit a revised (more favourable) quotation.
   Any change to the Scope is not a compensation event by definition (clause 60.1(1)).

The process has to be streamlined in order to reach a solution quickly before succeeding construction is superimposed on the 'defective' part.

3.9. Certification

The ECC does not contain terms such as 'practical completion', 'mechanical completion' or 'substantial completion'. Instead, it places on the *Project Manager* an obligation to decide the date when the *Contractor* has

- done all the work that the Scope states they are to do by the Completion Date
- corrected notified Defects that would have prevented the *Client* from using the *works* or Others from doing their work (clause 11.2(2)).

Having decided the date by which both of the above states have been reached (the date of Completion), the *Project Manager* then has a duty to certify Completion within 1 week of that date.

It is hoped that by expressly stating in the Scope the work that the *Contractor* is to do by the Completion Date, the uncertainty associated with such terms as 'substantial' and 'practical' completion will be avoided. The state of Completion clearly has not been reached if there remain uncorrected notified Defects that would prevent the *Client* from using the *works*.

The ECC adds a default: if the work that the *Contractor* is to do by the Completion Date is not stated in the Scope, Completion is when the *Contractor* has done all the work necessary for the *Client* to use the *works* and Others to do their work (clause 11.2(2)).

Clause 11.2(7) defines what is meant by a Defects Certificate, which is either

- a list of Defects that the *Supervisor* has notified before the *defects date* that the *Contractor* has **not** corrected or
- if there are no such Defects, a statement that there are none.

At first sight it might appear that the Defects Certificate is the equivalent of the certificate of completion of making good defects under JCT forms of contract. It is not! Those certificates are only issued when the *Contractor* has fulfilled their obligations to make good Defects, whereas under the ECC the Defects Certificate is issued on a set date as a **record** of whether or not the *Contractor* has fulfilled their obligations. If the *Contractor* has fulfilled their obligations, the Defects Certificate will simply contain a statement that there are no Defects to be corrected. If the *Contractor* has failed to fulfil their obligations, then the Defects Certificate will list the particular Defects that the *Contractor* has failed to correct by the end of the last *defect correction period*. The latter gives rise to the right for the *Project Manager* to have the uncorrected Defects corrected by others (see Section 3.10.4 below).

The timing of the issue of the Defects Certificate by the *Supervisor* is stated in clause 44.3: the *Supervisor* issues the Defects Certificate at the *defects date* if there are no notified Defects or otherwise at the earlier of

- the end of the last *defect correction period* (which may be later than the *defects date* if it commenced just before the *defects date* and therefore ends after it) or
- the date when all notified Defects have been corrected

The words:

'The *Client's* rights in respect of a Defect which the *Supervisor* has not found or notified are not affected by the issue of Defects Certificate' (clause 44.3) have been added to clarify that no transfer of liability occurs through the issue of the Defects Certificate.

The purpose, then, of the Defects Certificate is to put on record the state of the *works* at the date at which the *Contractor's* obligation to correct Defects expires. It is not therefore to be taken as a certificate of confirmation of fulfilment of the *Contractor's* obligations. However, the effect of the Defects Certificate is similar to that in other contracts, in that it triggers the release of the final part of retention money (where secondary Option X16 is used) and sets the date for the expiry of various other obligations.

It is appropriate at this time to consider the subject of latent defects; that is, defects that only appear after the Defects Certificate has been issued. In common with other standard forms of contract, the ECC does not expressly exclude the *Contractor's* liability for latent defects, and consequently the *Contractor's* liability follows the law applicable to the contract (subject to any limitation arising from clause X18.4 that only appears to apply to Defects due to the *Contractor's* design – not workmanship).

3.10. Enforcement
3.10.1 General

The fundamental significance of contracts and the law in general is enforceability by the courts. The term 'enforceability' as used in this context, however, is somewhat misleading in that it does not mean that the contract, or indeed ultimately the courts, will actually ensure that an agreement is fulfilled as intended. For example, a contract or the courts will not ensure that a contract to construct particular *works* will actually result in those works being constructed in accordance with the specified requirements. Enforceability, from the viewpoint of the *Client*, means that in the event of the *works* not being completed in accordance with the specified requirements, the contract will provide certain remedies or the courts will award financial compensation in respect of any loss or damage suffered by the *Client*. It is left to the disappointed *Client* to actually deal with the defects.

This final part of this chapter therefore deals with the contractual incentives and the remedies available to the *Client* when things do not go to plan and it becomes necessary to take 'enforcing' action. These remedies will be dealt with in an order starting with what might be considered the 'least serious' and working up to the 'most serious'. They will be considered under the following headings:

- incentivisation through certification
- removal of employees
- correction of Defects by Others
- low-performance damages
- termination of the *Contractor's* employment.

3.10.2 Incentivisation through certification

Although it has already been noted that the timing of the correction of pre-Completion Defects is largely a matter for the *Contractor*, there are powerful incentives introduced through the certification process (both of interim amounts due and of Completion) that make it in the *Contractor's* financial and commercial interest to correct Defects sooner rather than later (refer to Section 3.8.3 above).

3.10.3 The removal of employees

Since most quality problems can be traced back to people, be it due to the preparation of inadequate quality procedures or a failure to ensure that procedures are adhered to, it is reassuring to see that the ECC gives the *Project Manager* the power to instruct the *Contractor* to remove any person, having stated their reasons for doing so (refer to clause 24.2). If there was any doubt over whether the *Project Manager's* powers extended to include employees of Subcontractors, this is dispelled by the second sentence of clause 26.1, which states that 'this contract applies as if a Subcontractor's employees and equipment were the *Contractor's*'. The *Contractor* is obliged to ensure within 24 hours of the *Project Manager's* instruction that the person in question has no further connection with the contract. The *Contractor* may also be required to remove the person immediately.

3.10.4 The correction of Defects by Others

Clause 46.1 of the ECC is similar to the type of clause found in most construction contracts, entitling the *Client* to recover the cost of making Defects good if the *Contractor* has failed to correct them within a prescribed time, in this case the *defect correction period*. Since in the majority of cases uncorrected Defects will be a post-Completion issue, it will fall to the *Project Manager* to offset the cost of having the uncorrected Defects corrected by other people, against the release of the second half of the retention money, assuming Option X16 is included in the contract. The *retention percentage* should consequently be sufficient to produce an appropriate fund, which remains in the *Client's* hands until the *defects date* when the extent of the cost of uncorrected Defects is known.

Retention bonds, which are gaining in popularity with some *Clients* as an alternative to the traditional retention arrangements, are not directly catered for by the ECC, although they could be added through Option Z and by including the required form in the Scope.

3.10.5 Low-performance damages

Under the ECC the possible *Client's* remedies for low performance are as follows:

- the *Contractor* is required to correct Defects (clause 44.1; refer to Section 3.8.3 above)
- the contract price is reduced following the 'acceptance' by the *Project Manager* of a Defect that is not corrected (clause 45; refer to Section 3.8.5)
- the *Contractor* is liable for the cost of having Defects corrected by Others (clause 46.1; refer to Section 3.10.4)
- low-performance damages (secondary Option X17).

The low-performance damages secondary Option is most likely to be used in circumstances where the *Contractor* has full design responsibility and the *Client* has expressed their requirements for the completed works by way of performance criteria included in the Scope. They feature most commonly in process and plant contracts, but are occasionally found in construction contracts. Option X17 states that 'if a Defect included in the Defects Certificate shows low performance with respect to a performance level stated in the Contract Data [part one], the *Contractor* pays the amount of low performance damages stated in the Contract Data [part one]'. The consequence of this is that where the performance of the *works* in use fails to reach a specified level due to a design or other fault of the *Contractor* and the Defect is not corrected (i.e. it is listed in the Defects Certificate), the *Client* should be able to recover the damages they suffer in consequence, a genuine pre-estimate of which should be included by the *Client* in Contract Data part one.

Any deduction of low performance damages is made in the assessment of the amount due when the *Supervisor* issues the Defects Certificate, which again emphasises the need to consider making provision for the existence of an adequate retention fund at this time from which to set off any damages due.

3.10.6 Termination of the *Contractor's* employment Although this would be a last resort, the ECC does provide for the Contract to be terminated if, subject to a 4-week period to rectify a particular default, the *Contractor* has 'substantially failed to comply with its obligations' (clause 91.2 (R11)). Although the language used is fairly general, it could be that persistent failure by the *Contractor* to comply with the accepted quality plan, particularly where in reliance on such compliance the *Client* has reduced the levels of external supervision, would amount to a substantial failure by the *Contractor* to comply with their obligations. It would of course be helpful to the *Client's* case if they could demonstrate evidence of an intolerable level of Defects resulting from the *Contractor's* failure to comply with the quality plan.

Managing the Contract
ISBN 978-0-7277-6186-6

Chapter 4
Disputes and dispute resolution

Synopsis

This chapter

- emphasises the importance of early dispute resolution to the successful outcome of a contract
- considers the common sources of dispute
- considers how the ECC has been designed to reduce the incidence of disputes
- examines how the ECC provides for the resolution of disputes
- looks at the implications for the dispute resolution process as a result of the HGCR Act as amended
- looks at ECC changes in relation to adjudication.

4.1. Introduction

Over time, the construction industry has built up a reputation for being adversarial. The industry has spent millions of pounds in disputes that add no value to the construction process.

Most disputes at site level are founded on either

- differences in interpretation of the documents forming the contract (see Section 4.2.2 below) or
- differences of opinion over the financial and/or time effects of later events (see Section 4.2.3).

Such disputes divert considerable resources, sometimes at the expense of the ongoing construction. They cause budgetary uncertainty for clients and financial difficulties to contractors (and their subcontractors). Consequently, one of the few things that most people in the construction industry do agree on is that disputes are not a good thing, and most initiatives over recent years aimed at improving the performance of the construction industry have concluded that the adversarial culture has to change.

It should therefore come as no surprise that one of the fundamental objectives of the ECC was that its use should minimise the incidence of disputes and therefore improve the certainty about the outcome of the contract for both Parties. However, the ECC sensibly recognises that as long as two people can place different interpretations on or have different opinions on the same issue, then disputes will continue to arise. At the same time, given the potential damage such disputes present to the collaborative working principles upon which the ECC is founded, the NEC drafting team realised that disputes, having arisen, need to be resolved quickly and by a process that in principle is accepted as fair by both parties.

Fundamental objectives of the ECC are that its use should

- minimise the incidence of disputes
- improve certainty of outcome for both Parties.

4.2. How disputes arise

4.2.1 Introduction

Two of the main causes of disputes under the ECC are the Scope and the Site Information.

It is important that the information provided to the *Contractor* at the tender stage is as complete as it can possibly be. This means that a great deal of effort needs to be put into the preparation of information that will form part of the contract documents.

These requirements lead to a need for openness in the preparation of documentation. If the *Client* genuinely does not know about something, they should state so, and any later addition can be managed through the compensation event procedure. Alternatively, the *Client* could give assumptions upon which tenderers can base their bids. This philosophy is at odds with traditional professional training that encouraged the use of 'all-embracing' preambles to contract documents to cover everything stated and not stated. However, a *Contractor* is in no better position to manage the 'risk' than the *Client*, so there is no point in 'passing it on to them', because it will eventually come back to the *Client* to manage.

Another main area where risk arises is in the administration of the contract. An action/inaction under the contract can be grounds for a dispute to arise.

Ensure that information provided to the *Contractor* at the tender stage is as complete as possible.

Good documentation and good administration are essential in avoiding disputes.

The majority of disputes are probably avoidable but, before we consider how to avoid them, we need to understand better how they arise.

4.2.2 Interpretation of documents

The first source of disputes mentioned earlier is a difference in interpretation of the documents forming the contract.

The contract is drawn up to define what is required to be done in return for what payment; that is, the duties and responsibilities to be undertaken by each Party and (to some extent) what is to happen should they fail to exercise them. Where the definition of what is to be done is incomplete, the contract gives the *Client's* representative certain powers to supply further information and also to vary the work to be done. Risks, which may be encountered in the execution of the *works*, are allocated (both contractually and financially) between the Parties. The physical context within which the *works* are to be carried out and any constraints on the work to be done should also be stated.

Generally, it is the words used that matter – not those that could have been or even should have been used. The courts are inclined to take the words used at their face value, to assume that if used as they were intended, that the same word has the same meaning throughout and that if different words are used then different things are meant. They work on the basis that the words of the contract were agreed between both Parties to the contract, and that being so it is not open to either Party subsequently to complain that the responsibilities imposed are onerous.

It is convenient to think that the above applies only to the *conditions of contract*, but of course it applies to **all** the documents forming part of the contract. In the case of the ECC this means the documents stated as being part of the contract, as in the following:

- the form of contract/articles of agreement
- the core clauses and the main and secondary Option clauses of the ECC
- Contract Data part one and all documents referred to therein, principally the Scope and the Site Information
- Contract Data part two and all documents referred to therein, including any Scope for the *Contractor's* design, the first programme submitted for acceptance and the pricing document in the form of an *activity schedule* or *bill of quantities*.

Ironically, it is often the *conditions of contract* that prove to be the least fertile seedbed for disputes, probably explained by their careful legal drafting and (at least in the case of standard conditions) the Parties' familiarity with their meaning, their responsibilities under them and the recognised allocation of risk. The more common sources of dispute tend to be those documents that have to be prepared each time to suit the specific requirements of the individual contracts. With the ECC this means the Scope and the Site Information. It is worth considering the definition given to these supporting documents by the ECC (clauses 11.2(16) and 11.2(18)).

> The interpretation of documents applies to ALL the documents stated as being part of the contract, not just the *conditions of contract*.

4.2.2.1 The Scope

'Scope is information which
- specifies and describes the *works* or
- states any constraints on how the *Contractor* Provides the Works.' (clause 11.2(16))

The Scope will therefore typically include the general specification, the preliminaries, the materials and workmanship specification, the drawings, any *Client's* requirements in respect of parts of the *works* that the *Contractor* is to design, and any other document that describes what the *Contractor* is to construct and that describes any constraints on how they are to go about it.

Most disputes involving the Scope are therefore rooted in one of the following:

- the Scope is deficient in some respect, for example it is unclear as to who is responsible for certain actions (e.g. obtaining consents) or unclear as to the detail or the quality standards to be achieved

Table 4.1 The importance of the Scope in the ECC

Clause	Comments
11.2(6)	A part of the *works* not in accordance with the Scope is a Defect. It follows that the quality standards set out in the Scope provide the basis on which the existence of a Defect is judged. Problems arise when the Scope is silent on quality standards.
11.2(2)	Completion is when the *Contractor* has done all the work which the Scope states is to be done before the contractual Completion Date.
27.4	The *Contractor* is to act in accordance with the contract specific health and safety requirements stated in the Scope.
21.1	The *Contractor* is to design such parts of the *works* as stated in the Scope.
25.1	The *Contractor* is to share the Working Areas with Others as stated in the Scope.
41.2	The *Contractor* and the *Client* provide materials, facilities and samples for tests and inspections as stated in the Scope.

- there exists ambiguity or inconsistency in or between the documents that comprise the Scope
- the *Contractor* contends that the Scope requires them to do something that is illegal or impossible.

It is probably fair to say that in pursuit of the 'flexibility' objective, the ECC places greater reliance on the Scope as a source of supplementary information than more traditional contracts do on its equivalent. For example, details of testing are not included in the *conditions of contract*, but must be drafted by the *Client* and included in the Scope. It therefore follows that greater skill and care is required in the drafting of the Scope (in all its guises) if certain provisions of the ECC are to be effective. Some examples of the importance that the ECC attaches to the Scope are given in Table 4.1. For a full list, refer to Chapter 4 of Book Two.

> The interaction between the *conditions of contract* and the Scope means that disputes can occur when the Scope does not contain the information it should to give effect to the *conditions of contract*.

The quality of the drafting of the Work Information is very important. Some common problems include the following:

- A lack of precision as to what is required, a common example being quality standards that are described subjectively in terms such as 'to the satisfaction of the Engineer/Architect'.
- An inconsistency in style between the various parts of the Scope as a result of different people's contribution. There must be an overall editor/coordinator of the contract documents during their preparation if a 'patchwork quilt' effect is not to result.
- Ignorance of the fact that the Scope should be compatible with the *conditions of contract* and consequently the use of different terms and expressions that conflict with the responsibilities and risk allocation set out in the *conditions of contract*.
- A simple failure to appreciate how much information the *Contractor's* estimator needs in order to prepare a reliable tender. It must be realised that another party is committing themselves to translate the documents into physical reality for a price.

It has been said that the successful outcome of a contract is largely dependent on the managerial effort applied to the pre-planning and preparation of the contract documentation. Prevention of disputes is, after all, more economical than having to resolve them later. Given this fact, it is still incredible how poorly planned the pre-contract phase of most projects remains, with the preparation of tender documentation still viewed by many *Clients* and *Project Managers* as a simple activity of short duration squeezed in between the completion of design and the commencement of construction.

> The ECC places great emphasis on the Scope as a source of supplementary information, far more so than traditional contracts.

Having considered disputes rooted in the Scope, let us now consider the other information traditionally prepared by the *Client* and unique to each contract, namely the Site Information.

4.2.2.2 The Site Information

The ECC definition of the Site Information is simply information that describes the Site and its surroundings, the Site being that area within the *boundaries of the site* identified in the Contract Data. Consequently, the Site Information would include details of such matters as

- any existing buildings/other structures at the Site
- any existing buried or above-ground services
- soil characteristics
- the levels of interfaces between different geological strata
- groundwater levels
- the presence of any bodies of water within or surrounding the Site and seasonal water levels
- interpretative soil investigation reports.

It is easy to fall into the trap of thinking that Site Information relates to things (natural and artificial) that are pre-existing at the Site before any work is commenced. On a multi-contract project, details of the works constructed by the previous contractor become the Site Information for the follow-on contractor. Consequently, on a project for a new below-ground transportation system, the layout of the tunnels and the details of the tunnel linings, all constructed by the preceding 'civils' contractor, become the Site Information for the succeeding contractor engaged to install the mechanical and electrical system. For this reason, as well as to meet the requirements of the Construction (Design and Management) Regulations 2015, it is important to keep good records of the works actually being constructed by the different contractors on multi-contract projects.

On the basis that the Site Information should represent a factual account of the Site and its surroundings, it is surprising how many disputes arise from the encountering of physical conditions that, to use a common expression, 'could not reasonably have been foreseen by an experienced contractor'. So why should this be?

Historically, clients have invested too little money at the front end of projects, which is where any useful site investigation work is of most use, thereby ignoring the old maxim that 'money spent earlier buys more than money spent later'. In addition to the problem of not allocating sufficient monies to site investigation is the related problem of collecting information that is largely irrelevant to the construction of the works. A common problem is for the site investigation to focus on the design of the permanent works with little or no thought as to what information would be useful to the contractor in order to determine the most economic temporary works solution and working methods.

To emphasise the importance of comprehensive and relevant Site Information to the avoidance of disputes, consider the 'physical conditions risk' carried by the *Contractor* under the ECC. Putting weather conditions to one side (since these are dealt with separately), if the *Contractor* is to notify successfully for more money and/or time, they have to be able to persuade the *Project Manager* that the physical conditions actually encountered within the Site are so different that an experienced *Contractor* would have judged them to have such a small chance of occurring that it would have been unreasonable for them to have allowed for these. Recognising that this still leaves room for some interpretation, the ECC seeks to narrow the boundaries surrounding this provision by stating that

'In judging the physical conditions for the purpose of assessing a compensation event, the *Contractor* is assumed to have taken into account

- the Site Information,
- publicly available information referred to in the Site Information,
- information obtainable from a visual inspection of the Site and
- other information, which an experienced contractor could reasonably be expected to have or to obtain.' (clause 60.2)

Ignoring the obvious and the catch-all (third and fourth bullet points, respectively), it should be clear that the test of what should have been foreseeable by the experienced *Contractor* still relies heavily on information in or referred to in the Site Information, and the advice remains for *Clients* to buy the most comprehensive and relevant site investigation appropriate to the circumstances. However, to state a sum of money that should be spent on site investigation as a percentage of the value of the overall work can be misleading. It is far better to approach the subject from the risk analysis perspective.

Consider a new motorway contract where the designers are seeking to achieve a new vertical alignment that ensures a cut–fill balance; that is, using the excavated material derived from the cuttings as fill in the new embankment with a minimum of material to be disposed of off Site. It is clearly important to the *Client's* budget and programme for the contract to have a high level of confidence that sufficient quantities of acceptable material are present in the proposed cuttings. The consequence of this not being the case is the high cost of the disposal of quantities of unacceptable materials off Site (landfill tax included) and the additional cost of 'importing' acceptable fill materials to the Site. Given the 'risk exposure' in this instance, it might well prove desirable to invest in a thorough site investigation, and if necessary alter the vertical alignment to achieve the earthworks balance objective. Comprehensive site investigation is invariably a sound investment, since if it narrows the definition of the likely conditions to be encountered, it should accordingly reduce the amount of risk monies included in the *Contractor's* tender for what could otherwise be perceived as widely varying conditions.

So, what are the common sources of dispute associated with the Site Information?

- Where the Site Information does not accurately represent the actual physical conditions encountered. As noted, very often this is a result of an inadequate/irrelevant site investigation, but now and again it is just the result of something unexpected. This is more common with below-ground civil engineering works, where no matter how thorough the site investigation, until the *works* are actually executed the true nature of the conditions will never be known for certain. It was this feature of civil engineering works that has traditionally led to contracts for such work being accompanied by a *bill of quantities* containing provisional quantities of the work, all subject to admeasurement.
- Inconsistency or ambiguity in or between the documents that form part of the Site Information.

It should be noted that most disputes surrounding the Site Information are not black-and-white cases. It is for this reason that the ECC Guidance Notes introduce the concept of 'boundary limits'. These should be introduced to the contract through the use of secondary Option Z additional conditions.

Good, early and comprehensive site investigation for the permanent and temporary works is essential.

4.2.2.3 The Contract Data The final document mentioned earlier that is unique in its content to each project is the Contract Data, which forms part of the *conditions of contract*. It comes in two parts, part one prepared by the *Client* and sent out with the invitation to tender letter and accompanying tender documentation, and part two prepared by the *Contractor* and submitted with the tender submission. Its purpose is to provide key information as required by the *conditions of contract* and that is specific to a particular contract. It is absolutely key to the effective operation of the ECC that the terms in italics contained in the *conditions of contract* are given their meaning by the related entry in the Contract Data. For example, the following are addressed in the Contract Data:

- the main Option and secondary Options applicable to the particular contract
- the names of the *Client, Contractor, Project Manager, Supervisor* and *Adjudicator*
- where to find the documents comprising the Scope and the Site Information
- the *starting date, access dates* and *completion date(s)*
- the *method of measurement* (if an ECC main Option using a *bill of quantities* applies)
- the amount of delay damages (Option X7) payable by the *Contractor* if the *works* are late and the amount of low-performance damages (Option X17) payable if the *works* do not meet stated performance levels
- the names of the *Contractor's* key people
- any Scope in respect of designs for which the *Contractor* is responsible
- the identity of the *activity schedule* or *bill of quantities* as appropriate, together with the tendered total of the Prices
- the identity of the first programme to be submitted.

The ECC provides a pro forma Contract Data, and consequently the likelihood of getting it wrong should be small, most errors arising from a misunderstanding of the information to be inserted. Getting it wrong is serious, however, since unlike the Scope, which can be changed by an instruction given by the *Project Manager*, once the contract has been let, the Contract Data can only be changed by agreement between the *Client* and the *Contractor*.

One common mistake made by drafters of the documents comprising the ECC is to mix up information between the Site Information and the Scope, for example giving information describing the Site and its surroundings in documents identified by the Contract Data as being the Scope (and vice versa). This is something that must be avoided (see Chapter 4 of Book Two).

> The *Client* might have commissioned the most comprehensive and relevant site investigations possible, but if they then include the findings in a document referred to as the Scope, they will not be able to rely on it as Site Information when seeking to counter a compensation event notification from the *Contractor* contending changed physical conditions.

It is essential to ensure that the data in Contract Data part one and Contract Data part two are complete. It is not uncommon to find that some data are not inserted by the *Contractor* at the time of tender, for example components of cost for the Short Schedule of Cost Components.

> Ensure that the Contract Data has been fully completed at the tender and tender assessment stages. The Scope and Site Information should be kept separate. Failure to do so might have implications on how a compensation event is assessed.

4.2.3 The cost and time effects of disputes

The second source of dispute identified is differences of opinion over the financial and/or time effects of events that arise once the contract has been let. In this instance, since the hurdle as to whether entitlement exists contractually for any particular case has been overcome, it remains only to establish its financial and time effects.

Traditionally, price-based contracts have sought to assess the financial effects of variations and other events at the client's risk as follows:

- If the nature of the work affected by the 'event' and the conditions under which it is required to be undertaken are unchanged from those pertaining when the contractor prepared their tender, then such rates would be used to value the effects of the variation or change.

- If one or other of the nature or the conditions is dissimilar, then the contract rates and prices are used as the basis for assessing the value of the variation or change.
- If neither the nature of the work nor the conditions are similar, then the client's representative would be responsible for ascertaining a fair evaluation, but in doing so would seek to ensure that as far as possible the valuation was still related to the contractor's original contract rates and prices.
- As a last resort in circumstances where none of the above were feasible, the variation or change would be valued on a cost-plus or 'day work' basis.

This process resulted in many disputes over the applicability of the contract rates, usually contained in a bill of quantities, a document based on the misapprehension that all of a contractor's costs are proportional to the quantities of the various elements of the work.

A contractor losing money or seeking to earn inflated profits could always be relied upon to come up with all sorts of plausible reasons why the contract rates were not applicable to the varied work. The client's representative often found it difficult to counter such arguments, given the veil that the bill of quantities throws across the contractor's true costs and the manner in which they are incurred.

If agreeing the financial effects of change was a challenge, then agreement of the time effects was nigh on impossible given the traditional scant regard paid to monitoring progress against an original and meaningful programme and it being in the contractor's interest to address the delaying effects for which the client was responsible later rather than sooner, once delays caused by their own inefficiencies were less prominent in the memory of the client's representative.

It is perhaps sad that until very recently far more space on construction industry bookshop shelves and far more seminar time were devoted to the subject of 'claimsmanship' than to improving the performance of the construction industry for the benefit of its customers. Although it looks like this trend has altered, disputes over both money and time still comprise a large proportion of the total of all disputes at the site level.

4.3. How the ECC seeks to reduce the incidence of disputes

When designing the ECC the drafters intended it to be flexible and clear and to promote good management. One example of this is the avoidance in the contract of such phrases as 'in the opinion of the Engineer'. Instead, the duties of the *Project Manager* are clearly set out, and the criteria on which their decisions are to be based are stated specifically, not left to a general concept of acceptability.

In many instances, the ECC will serve to reduce the incidence of disputes by virtue of its two founding principles, both of which have a major impact upon the objectives of stimulating good management. These principles are

- foresight applied collaboratively mitigates problems and shrinks risk
- clear division of function and responsibility helps accountability and motivates people to play their part.

Some practical examples of how these principles serve to reduce the incidence of disputes follow.

4.3.1 Early warning

The early warning provision of the ECC places an obligation on both the *Project Manager* and the *Contractor* to give to the other a notification of any matter that could increase the price that the *Client* pays, delay Completion or impact on the finished quality of the *works* or delay meeting a Key Date. The *Contractor* and the *Project Manager* may also give an early warning of any other matter that could increase the *Contractor's* total cost. Early warning of a matter for which a compensation event has previously been notified is not required. This is intended to be a practical device to stimulate early joint consideration of unforeseen problems.

Joint consideration of the problem should lead to joint agreement as to the best solution, and consequently the necessary action to avoid the problem or reduce its impact. In addition to shrinking the risk to the price, the programme and the quality of the *works*, the early warning provisions, by involving the *Project Manager* in the decision-making, reduce the possibility of them deciding at a later date with the wisdom of hindsight that the *Contractor* did not deal with the problem in the most cost- and/or time-effective manner.

4.3.2 Valuing changes

Many disputes arise over the assessment of the financial and time effects of variations and other changes at the *Client's* risk under the contract. These disputes invariably centre on the applicability of the contract rates to the changed situation and the ineffective use of a programme to monitor progress and plan the future work.

Under the ECC, the traditional basis of valuing variations using tendered bill of quantities rates is discarded in favour of valuation according to the full effect of the variation on timing and methods of work, and the use of resources (although rates can be used by agreement in the assessment of compensation events). Such a means of valuation relies on the *Contractor* maintaining a comprehensive, realistic and up-to-date plan for the remaining work that they are obliged to do by the ECC and for which serious sanctions apply in the event that they fail to do so. The side-benefit of these requirements is to eliminate disputes over the applicability of tendered rates for pricing variations and to reduce the likelihood of disputes over the time effect of those same variations.

4.3.3 Clear division of function and responsibility

The ECC recognises that if risk is placed on a Party to the contract, that Party is motivated to minimise its effect and use risk allocation to encourage good management in the Parties most likely to be able to respond.

For example, the contractor is traditionally assumed to have inspected the site and carried out their own site investigation. This does not motivate the client to do sufficient site investigation to establish the effect of ground conditions on construction cost. The ECC does not state that the *Client* should do more site investigations, as this would have little impact. Instead it is stated that the *Contractor* is to assume that the ground conditions will be as they are described to them in the tender documents (the Site Information).

Consequently, if only minimal site investigation has been done, the *Contractor* could base their price on an erroneous view of the sub-surface conditions. As this will increase the *Client's* risk of later programme delays and extra cost, the *Client* is more strongly motivated to investigate sufficiently. The side-benefit of course is that if the *Client* is motivated to do a comprehensive site investigation, the likelihood of disputes arising over changed conditions and their effect on the *works* must be reduced.

Staying with site investigations and physical conditions, it was stated earlier that disputes rooted in different interpretations placed on the Site Information are rarely black-and-white affairs. This is due, in part, to the difficulty in defining precisely the boundary between the physical condition risk carried by the *Contractor* and that by the *Client*. This difficulty is exacerbated by the use in construction contracts of such terms as 'those physical conditions which could not reasonably have been foreseen by an experienced *Contractor*' to describe the risk carried by the *Client*. A simple example of the problem will illustrate the difficulty.

The Site Information includes three borehole logs, which indicate that in three separate locations the depth of the existing topsoil at the Site was 100, 200 and 350 mm, respectively. Is the *Contractor* deemed to have included in the price for excavating existing topsoil across the Site up to 350 mm thick, an average of 217 mm thick across the Site or some other permutation of the numbers depending on the precise location of the boreholes?

The ECC Guidance Notes have recognised the potential for such issues to give rise to disputes, and so they suggest the inclusion in the contract of 'boundary limits' between the risks carried by the *Client* and the *Contractor*; that is, to state what tenderers should allow for in their tenders.

In our topsoil example this could be done by stating in the Scope that the *Contractor* shall be deemed to have allowed in the tendered total of the Prices for excavating a prescribed volume of topsoil with a thickness in the range of 100–350 mm. Additionally, a small tolerance, say $\pm 5\%$, could be stated to apply to the prescribed volume to avoid compensation events for insignificant changes in quantity. Tenderers will then be able to tender on a common basis knowing that they must allow in their pricing for the occurrence of physical conditions within the stated boundary limits. The same principles can of course be applied to such physical conditions as soil characteristics, the level of the rock–soil interface, groundwater levels, permeability limits and overbreak in rock excavation.

4.3.4 Reducing disputes in the Scope and Site Information

This section examines how the ECC attempts to head off potential disputes centring on deficient/inadequate Works and Site Information, looking individually at cases where

- the Scope is unclear as to what is to be done
- there exists ambiguity or inconsistency in or between the documents comprising the Scope
- the *Contractor* contends that the Scope requires them to do something that is illegal or impossible
- there exist inconsistencies within the Site Information (including the information referred to in it).

4.3.4.1 Scope descriptions

This situation is where the Scope does not provide a full description of what is to be done by the *Contractor* or does not describe adequately the constraints under which the work is to be done.

For example, in a contract where the *Client* is responsible for all design, the Scope might be silent on the subject of what tests are necessary to verify the quality of a particular component or the construction tolerances applicable. In such instances, it falls to the *Project Manager* to remedy this deficiency as part of their duty to ensure that the completed *works* meet the *Client's* objectives in terms of quality. Clause 14.3 of the ECC gives the *Project Manager* the power to instruct a change to the Scope, and, in the example referred to, the *Project Manager* would instruct the *Contractor* as to what tests were necessary, or the construction tolerance that was applicable. Such an instruction, being a change to the Scope, is of course a compensation event (clause 60.1(1)), and the *Contractor* would therefore be entitled to an assessment of time and money, which, if nothing else, emphasises the importance of getting the Scope right in the first instance.

> Get the Scope right!
>
> Deficiencies in the Scope may lead to compensation events.

4.3.4.2 Conflicts within the Scope

The second situation is where separate parts of the Scope might in themselves be clear as to what is to be done but, unfortunately, conflict with one another – for example the same reinforcement bars called up as two different diameters in the reinforcement schedules and on the reinforced concrete detail drawings. The ECC does not use a hierarchical arrangement of the contract documents, giving precedence to those higher up the hierarchy to resolve such ambiguities. Instead, where such ambiguities and inconsistencies exist in or between the documents comprising the Scope, the ECC places the responsibility on the *Project Manager* to give an instruction resolving the ambiguity or inconsistency, for example by advising the *Contractor* what the *Client*/designer actually requires (clause 17.1). If the resolution of the ambiguity or inconsistency requires an instruction that changes the Scope, the *contra proferentum* rule applies, which interprets any ambiguous or inconsistent statements in a contract against the party responsible for their preparation.

> To put this into a practical context, using the reinforcement example above, if the reinforcement schedule showed 32 mm bars and the reinforcement detail drawing for the same bars indicated a diameter of 40 mm, then if the *Project Manager* confirms the latter as being required, the effect of the ensuing compensation event would be assessed as if the Prices and the Completion Date and the Key Dates were for the interpretation most favourable to the *Contractor*; that is, they would be deemed to have allowed in their original tender price for the smaller bars.

The ECC has no hierarchy of documents.

The *contra proferentum* rule applies against the *Client* if the Scope contains conflicting information, since ambiguities and inconsistencies in wording are construed against the drafter.

4.3.4.3 The Scope requires an illegal action

The third situation is where the *Contractor* notifies the *Project Manager* that they consider the Scope requires them to do something that is illegal (e.g. to flout the building regulations) or impossible (e.g. to construct a bored tunnel causing absolutely no settlement). If, having reviewed the situation, the *Project Manager* agrees, they give an instruction changing the Scope appropriately (clause 17.2). This, of course, would be a compensation event (clause 60.1(1)).

4.3.4.4 Inconsistencies within the Site Information

Finally, where the Site Information contains inconsistencies within itself or between it and other information referred to in it: for example, one part of the Site Information shows the Site to be clear of all buried services while another part shows a high-pressure gas main crossing the Site. Again, the *contra proferentum* rule applies, clause 60.3 stating that 'the *Contractor* is assumed to have taken into account the physical conditions more favourable to doing the work'; that is, in this case to have assumed the Site to be clear of all buried services.

The *contra proferentum* rule applies to the Site Information.

4.3.5 Conclusion

All of the above are examples of 'self-help' remedies contained within the ECC, facilitating the removal of the uncertainty as to what is to be done in particular circumstances and in doing so reducing the potential for disputes.

Before concluding this section, it is worth countering the concerns from many quarters that by using the ECC there is a risk that claims on contractual matters will increase because the contract is relatively untried, the language is unfamiliar and the contract has never been tested in the courts. The ECC had more legal checking before publication than any of the traditional standard forms preceding it. It was drafted to eliminate known problems associated with traditional contracts that have come before the courts. All the well-known court cases that hinged upon the wording of a traditional contract have been taken into account in drafting the ECC so that the same matter could not come up again when the ECC was used. In addition, the fact that it has not been tested in court is extremely positive – it means the contract has not been so troublesome that a court has had to resolve conflicts.

We will now consider in the final section of this chapter the situation where, despite all the efforts of both parties, and the self-help remedies contained within the ECC, a dispute actually arises.

4.4. Dispute resolution under the ECC
4.4.1 General

The ECC caters for dispute resolution in three ways, as shown in Figure 4.1.

The NEC had catered for adjudication as a dispute resolution procedure prior to legislation promulgated in the UK mandating the use of adjudication in construction contracts (as defined). This procedure is still available in the ECC, and is described in Option W1.

The HGCR Act mandated adjudication for construction contracts let after 1 May 1998, and the procedure for this type of adjudication is described in Option W2.

A third option for dispute resolution is the use of a Dispute Avoidance Board in place of adjudication, and this procedure is described in Option W3.

All three Options for resolving and avoiding disputes have as their last tier of resolution the *tribunal*, which is usually either arbitration or the courts, and the *Client* states their choice in Contract Data part one. Table 4.2 describes the three Options in broad detail.

Figure 4.1 Levels of dispute resolution in Options W1, W2 and W3

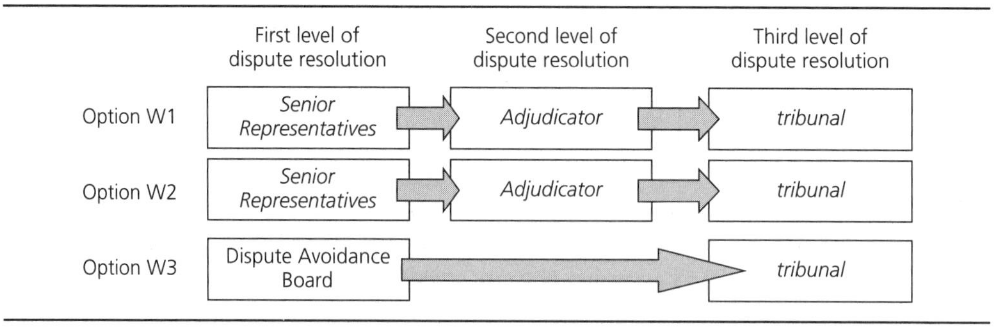

Table 4.2 Options in the ECC for dispute resolution

	Option W1	Option W2	Option W3
When is it used?	Used when the HGCR Act does *not* apply	Used when the HGCR Act applies	Used when the HGCR Act does *not* apply
What preparations are made?	The *Adjudicator* is appointed by the Parties under the NEC4 Dispute Resolution Service Contract at the *starting date*	The *Adjudicator* is appointed by the Parties under the NEC4 Dispute Resolution Service Contract at the *starting date*	The Dispute Avoidance Board is appointed by the Parties under the NEC4 Dispute Resolution Service Contract at the *starting date*
What actions are taken by the dispute resolver during the period of the contract?			The Dispute Avoidance Board visits the Site at stated intervals, inspects the progress of the *works* and becomes aware of any potential differences
To whom is a dispute referred?	A dispute is referred to the *Senior Representatives*	If the Parties agree, a dispute is referred to the *Senior Representatives*	A difference is referred to the Dispute Avoidance Board
What procedures are in place?	Each Party and the *Senior Representatives* follow the procedure described and comply with the timescales required	Each Party and the *Senior Representatives* follow the procedure described and comply with the timescales required	Each Party and the Dispute Avoidance Board follow the procedure described and comply with the timescales required
When can a dispute be referred to the next level of dispute resolution?	If the dispute is not resolved by the *Senior Representatives*, it is referred to and decided by the *Adjudicator*	A dispute can be referred to the *Adjudicator* by either Party at any time, irrespective of whether the dispute has been referred to the *Senior Representatives*	If the dispute is not resolved by the *Senior Representatives*, it is referred to and decided by the *Adjudicator*. Only issues not agreed by the *Senior Representatives* are referred to the *Adjudicator*
What disputes can be referred to the next level of dispute resolution?	Only issues not agreed by the *Senior Representatives* are referred to the *Adjudicator*	A dispute can be referred to the *Adjudicator* by either Party at any time	A Party may not refer a dispute to the *tribunal* unless a difference has first been referred to the Dispute Avoidance Board
What procedures are in place?	The Parties and the *Adjudicator* follow the procedure described and comply with the timescales	The Parties and the *Adjudicator* follow the procedure described and comply with the timescales	
When does a dispute go to the next level of dispute resolution?	A Party who is dissatisfied with the *Adjudicator*'s decision may refer that matter to the *tribunal*	A Party who is dissatisfied with the *Adjudicator*'s decision may refer that matter to the *tribunal*	A Party who is dissatisfied with the Dispute Avoidance Board's recommendation may refer that matter to the *tribunal*

> The ECC caters for adjudication on contracts that **do not** fall within the definition of a construction contract or are outside the UK.
>
> Secondary Option Y(UK)2 should be chosen for contracts that fall within the definition of a construction contract.

4.4.2 Option W1 first tier – *Senior Representatives* The first dispute resolution tier in Option W1 is to refer a dispute to the *Senior Representatives*. Both the *Client* and the *Contractor* have the opportunity to name the people whom they wish to represent their interests in the case of a dispute.

Contract Data part one

If Option W1 or W2 is used

The *Senior Representatives* of the *Client* are

Name (1) ....

Address for communications ....

Address for electronic communications ....

Name (2) ....

Address for communications ....

Address for electronic communications ....

Contract Data part two

If Option W1 or W2 is used

The *Senior Representatives* of the *Contractor* are

Name (1) ....

Address for communications ....

Address for electronic communications ....

Name (2) ....

Address for communications ....

Address for electronic communications ....

Three matters may be notified by either Party, and one further matter can only be notified by the *Client*.

- The *Contractor* may refer these matters to the *Senior Representatives*:
  (*a*) an action or inaction of the *Project Manager* or the *Supervisor*
  (*b*) an assessment of Defined Cost that is treated as correct
  (*c*) any other matter.
- The *Client* may refer these matters to the *Senior Representatives*:
  (*a*) an action or inaction of the *Project Manager* or the *Supervisor*
  (*b*) an assessment of Defined Cost that is treated as correct
  (*c*) any other matter
  (*d*) a programme, compensation event or quotation for a compensation event which is treated as having been accepted.

The *Senior Representatives* work together as one body to

- review each Party's statement of case (clause W1.1(2) does not actually provide that the Parties submit their statement of case to the *Senior Representatives*, only to each other, but the statements must also go to the *Senior Representatives* if they are to review the dispute)
- attend as many meetings and use any procedure they consider necessary to try to resolve the disputes within the time allowed (no more than 3 weeks)
- produce a list of the issues agreed and the issues not agreed.

The ECC provides that if the dispute is not resolved by the *Senior Representatives*, it is referred to and decided by the *Adjudicator*. There is no choice involved. However, this is softened slightly by clause W1.3(1), which provides that a Party who disputes any issue not agreed by the *Senior Representatives* issues a notice of adjudication and refers the dispute to the *Adjudicator* (note that the clause does not state who refers the dispute to the *Adjudicator*, but it is likely to be the disputing Party).

4.4.2.1 Who should be selected as a *Senior Representative*

People who can view things fairly dispassionately should be selected, such as a managing director. Also, consider having a lawyer on the team to assess legal risks, someone who can see beyond the immediate budget (because in the end it's all about money), and someone who can see where their team has failed to deliver and can address the issues that arise without casting blame.

4.4.2.2 Who should be selected as an *Adjudicator*

Although the *Adjudicator* is appointed at the *starting date* of the construction contract, the *Adjudicator* only becomes involved when a dispute arises.

Their fees are shared between the Parties regardless of their decision and regardless of which Party refers the dispute.

The *Adjudicator's* decision is final and binding unless revised by the *tribunal*.

A dispute cannot be referred to the *tribunal* unless it has first been referred to adjudication.

Construction projects are complex, and disputes can arise on technical or commercial issues. On the technical side, a dispute may involve specialist work such as geotechnical engineering, or specialist engineering systems that need to meet prescriptive performance tests.

Therefore, even the most experienced professional acting as an *Adjudicator* is unlikely to be an expert or knowledgeable on everything.

Some people suggest having a number of adjudicators named to cover engineering and commercial aspects. However, this should be unnecessary since the named *Adjudicator* should have the relevant experience/competence to draw upon the technical assistance of others.

The *Adjudicator's* name should be inserted in Contract Data part one.

The *Adjudicator* only becomes involved when a dispute arises.

Appointed jointly by the *Client* and the *Contractor* on the NEC4 Dispute Resolution Service Contract.

Adjudication fees are shared equally irrespective of their decision.

4.4.3 Option W2 first tier – *Senior Representatives*

The first dispute resolution tier in Option W2 is to refer a dispute to the *Senior Representatives* – but only if both Parties agree to do this. Both the *Client* and the *Contractor* have the opportunity to name the people whom they wish to represent their interests in the case of a dispute.

Contract Data part one

If Option W1 or W2 is used

The *Senior Representatives* of the *Client* are

      Name (1) ....

      Address for communications ....

      Address for electronic communications ....

      Name (2) ....

      Address for communications ....

      Address for electronic communications ....

Contract Data part two

If Option W1 or W2 is used

The *Senior Representatives* of the *Contractor* are

      Name (1) ....

      Address for communications ....

      Address for electronic communications ....

      Name (2) ....

      Address for communications ....

      Address for electronic communications ....

There is no restriction on the types of matters that can be referred to the *Senior Representatives*, and there is no absolute obligation or requirement to refer disputes to the *Senior Representatives* prior to adjudication, as legislation provides that disputes can be referred to the *Adjudicator* at any time.

The *Senior Representatives* work together as one body to

- review each Party's statement of case (clause W2.1(2) does not actually provide that the Parties submit their statement of case to the *Senior Representatives*, only to each other, but the statements must also go to the *Senior Representatives* if they are to review the dispute)
- attend as many meetings and use any procedure they consider necessary to try to resolve the disputes within the time allowed (no more than 3 weeks)
- produce a list of the issues agreed and the issues not agreed.

The ECC provides that if the dispute is not resolved by the *Senior Representatives*, it is referred to and decided by the *Adjudicator*. There is no choice involved.

See Section 4.4.2.1 above regarding the selection of *Senior Representatives*.

4.4.4 Option W2 second tier – adjudication after the HGCR Act

The NEC is an international contract, and, as such, a national requirement for the HGCR Act as amended, which is a UK-specific requirement, should not be contained within the core clauses of the contract. Therefore, Option W1 or W3 is to be used except in the UK, when the HGCR Act as amended applies. (Note: not all construction projects in the UK fall under the HGCR Act – see sections 104–107 of the act.)

Option W1 or W3 can be chosen for non-UK contracts and those contracts in the UK that fall outside of the definition of a construction contract for the purposes of the HGCR Act as amended.

Option W2 is to be used in the UK when the HGCR Act as amended applies, and must be used with secondary Option Y(UK)2, which ensures compliance with the requirements of section 110 ('Dates for payment'), section 111 ('Requirement to pay notified sum'), section 112 ('Right to suspend performance for non-payment') and section 116 ('Reckoning of periods of time').

The *Client* is required to identify the *Adjudicator* in Contract Data part one.

Contract Data part one

If Option W1 or W2 is used

The *Adjudicator* is

    Name ....

    Address for communications ....

    Address for electronic communications ....

The *Adjudicator nominating body* is ....

As with adjudication under Option W1, the *Adjudicator* is appointed jointly by the *Client* and the *Contractor* under the NEC Dispute Resolution Service Contract at the *starting date*.

Unlike Option W1, there is no restriction on the types of dispute that can be referred to adjudication; but the procedure follows similar lines to Option W1. The procedure below is drafted in the case of the *Contractor* referring a dispute:

1 The *Senior Representatives* do not resolve a dispute.	OR	1 A Party refers a dispute to the *Adjudicator* whether or not the dispute has been referred to the *Senior Representatives*.

2 The *Contractor* gives a notice of adjudication to the other Party and sends a copy of the notice of adjudication to the *Adjudicator*.

3 Within 3 days of the receipt of the notice of adjudication, the *Adjudicator* tells the *Client* and the *Contractor* if they can decide the dispute.

4 Within 7 days of a Party giving a notice of adjudication, it refers the dispute to the *Adjudicator*, and provides information to the *Adjudicator* and the other Party. Further information must be provided within 14 days of referral.

Within 28 days of the referral, the *Adjudicator* notifies their decision together with their reasons.

All periods may be extended subject to certain procedures.

See Section 4.4.2.2 above regarding the selection of an *Adjudicator*.

4.4.5 Option W3 first tier – the Dispute Avoidance Board

The first tier of dispute resolution in Option W3 is a Dispute Avoidance Board to whom differences are referred. The members for the Dispute Avoidance Board are chosen by the *Client* and the *Contractor* using Contract Data parts one and two, and the Dispute Avoidance Board is appointed by the *Client* and the *Contractor* under the NEC Dispute Resolution Service Contract at the *starting date*.

Contract Data part one

If Option W3 is used

The *Client's* nomination for the Dispute Avoidance Board is

    Name ....

    Address for electronic communications ....

The Dispute Avoidance Board visit the Site at intervals not longer than .... months

The *Dispute Avoidance Board nominating body* is ....

Contract Data part two

If Option W3 is used

The *Contractor's* nomination for the Dispute Avoidance Board is

    Name ....

    Address for electronic communications ....

Unlike the *Senior Representatives* and the *Adjudicator*, the Dispute Avoidance Board is more involved actively in the ongoing progress of the *works* and takes a more proactive role with regards to disputes, As such, the *Client* and the *Contractor* should consider carefully whom they would like to make decisions for them and what their qualifications and experience should be. The Dispute Avoidance Board may not include people whom the *Client* would put forward as an *Adjudicator*.

The Dispute Avoidance Board

- visits the Site regularly after the start of the contract unless the *Client* and the *Contractor* agree that a visit is not necessary, and they make extra visits when the Parties ask them to (note that the wording in the ECC refers to one visit only, so the Dispute Avoidance Board must visit at the intervals stated and the Parties' decision that the Dispute Avoidance Board can forego a visit does not mean that no further visits need take place)
- inspects the progress of the *works* during visits and uses the time to become aware of any potential differences – a very proactive approach and one designed to be objective
- adheres to the site visit agenda proposed by the Parties
- prepares a note of its visit
- assists the Parties in resolving differences before they become disputes
- provides a recommendation for resolving differences unless the Parties have resolved the difference by the end of the Site visit
- can take the initiative in reviewing potential disputes, including asking the Parties to provide further information.

The members of the Dispute Avoidance Board, their employees and agents are not liable to the Parties for any action or failure unless the action or failure was in bad faith (clause W3.1(7)).

The overall Dispute Avoidance Board procedure is described in Table 4.3.

Before a dispute is referred to the *tribunal*, it must be referred to the Dispute Avoidance Board as a difference. A Party who is dissatisfied with the Dispute Avoidance Board's recommendation may refer a dispute to the *tribunal*.

Table 4.3 The Dispute Avoidance Board procedure

Clause	Comment
W3.2(1)	A difference arising under or in connection with the contract is referred to the Dispute Avoidance Board
W3.2(2)	Between 2 and 4 weeks after notification of the difference to the other Party and the *Project Manager*, differences are notified and referred to the Dispute Avoidance Board The Dispute Avoidance Board assists the Parties in resolving differences before they become disputes
W3.2(3)	The Parties make available to the Dispute Avoidance Board ■ copies of the contract ■ progress reports ■ any other material they consider relevant to any difference that they wish the Dispute Avoidance Board to consider in advance of the visit to Site
W3.2(4)	The Dispute Avoidance Board ■ visits the Site and inspect the *works* ■ reviews all potential disputes and helps the Parties to settle them without the need for the dispute to be formally referred ■ prepares a note of its visit ■ provides a recommendation for resolving the difference – unless the Parties have resolved the difference by the end of the Site visit
W3.2(5)	The Dispute Avoidance Board can take the initiative in reviewing potential disputes, including asking the Parties to provide further information

4.4.5.1 Selection of the Dispute Resolution Board

Care should be taken in the selection of those people who are to sit on the Dispute Resolution Board. Does the person selected have the required competencies and skills to resolve disputes as they arise?

4.4.6 The *tribunal* – last tier for Options W1, W2 and W3

The *tribunal* is the second formal level of dispute resolution in the ECC. The *tribunal* is chosen by the *Client* (by an appropriate insertion in Contract Data part one), and would normally be either arbitration or the courts.

Contract Data part one

If the tribunal is arbitration

The *arbitration procedure* is ....

The place where arbitrations is to be held is ....

The person or organisation who will choose an arbitrator if the Parties cannot agree a choice or if the *arbitration procedure* does not state who selects an arbitrator is ....
....

4.5. Dispute resolution – general comments and observations

There are generally two schools of thought about adjudication:

- the adjudication is in the contract to be used
- adjudication is a failure (because the dispute has not been resolved prior to the adjudication process).

In relation to the first point, many 'enlightened' *Clients* see adjudication as a failure, and introduce through Option Z (additional conditions) clauses and procedures that deal with dispute resolution in a contract. This usually revolves around the idea of a dispute being resolved at the lowest level possible and there being an 'escalation' process for the more difficult issues. Only after the parties have exhausted this in a structured timescale is adjudication used.

This type of arrangement is often found in partnering and frame-working arrangements.

Figure 4.2 shows an example of the 'steps' in the escalation of a dispute.

4.5.1 'Star chambers' and the like

A 'star chamber' is simply an interim dispute resolution process according to which, if the Parties fail to agree at the lowest level, then the dispute will ultimately be resolved by the star chamber. The star chamber comprises the managing directors or other senior executives of the two Parties. Some commentators consider that such a chamber also needs an independent representation whenever it is unable to agree a decision.

If the issue gets as far as the star chamber, each party will be given an opportunity to resolve the issue at the lowest level, usually to a prescribed timescale.

After having been given time to resolve the issue at the lowest level, each party will be given a set period, say 2 weeks, in which to compile the facts as they see them. Each side then also presents this information in a 15–20-minute presentation. The star chamber members then deliberate on the issue and give their decision.

The process relieves the lower levels of management from making decisions on disputed items, and gets them resolved so that they can concentrate on their role in the project (adding value), rather than being distracted from their role.

The authors' own experience is that having to present your argument/reasoning on why something is or is not a compensation event is daunting, especially if your audience is your company's managing director or client.

It is interesting to note that such a procedure does encourage resolution at the lowest level. People tend not to want to appear unable to resolve issues perceived as being confrontational.

Options W1 and W2 include for a dispute being referred to *Senior Representatives*, chosen by both Parties at the tender stage, before the dispute is formally referred to adjudication, and the

Figure 4.2 Dispute escalation

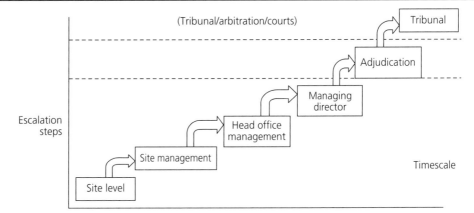

procedures described are similar to a star chamber arrangement. Note, however, that in Option W2 the reference to the *Senior Representatives* prior to adjudication cannot be enforced due to the HGCR Act allowing for adjudication at any time, but the facility to attempt a resolution prior to a formal reference nevertheless indicates a willingness to do so.

4.5.2 Good information and records – how the dispute resolver will judge the information

It is essential to keep good records and information in a structured way, as required by the ECC.

The *Adjudicator* and the other dispute resolution boards such as the *Senior Representatives* and the Dispute Avoidance Board will review the actions/inaction of the Parties based upon the information and records existing at the time that the issue/dispute arose.

The added benefit of good information and records is that if/when a dispute arises, you will not be involved in hours or days of documentation retrieval. This is especially true where IT has been harnessed to control the administration of change.

4.5.3 The *Adjudicator*

The *Client* will insert in section 1, 'General', in Contract Data part one the name of the *Adjudicator*. Before naming the *Adjudicator*, the *Client* should check that the *Adjudicator* has no conflicts of interest with the Parties and that they have the relevant experience, qualifications and competency.

Some *Clients* have a list of *Adjudicators* from which to choose (note that having an *Adjudicator* on a retainer basis defeats the purpose of an independent arbiter of disputes), others simply leave it open for the *Adjudicator* to be selected by the president of the ICE or other professional body. Most of the professional bodies keep a register of approved adjudicators.

It is essential to name the *Adjudicator* in the contract prior to contract execution. If the Parties are already in dispute, it may become unlikely that they will agree the name of the *Adjudicator* for contracts where 'to be agreed' has been inserted against the *Adjudicator* in the Contract Data.

4.5.3.1 When should the *Adjudicator* become involved?

Although the *Adjudicator* is appointed at the *starting date* of the construction contract, the *Adjudicator* only becomes involved when a dispute arises.

Their fees are shared between the Parties regardless of their decision and regardless of which Party refers the dispute.

Managing the Contract
ISBN 978-0-7277-6186-6

ICE Publishing: All rights reserved
http://dx.doi.org/10.1680/mc.61866.079

Index